THE EVIDENCE OF EVOLUTION

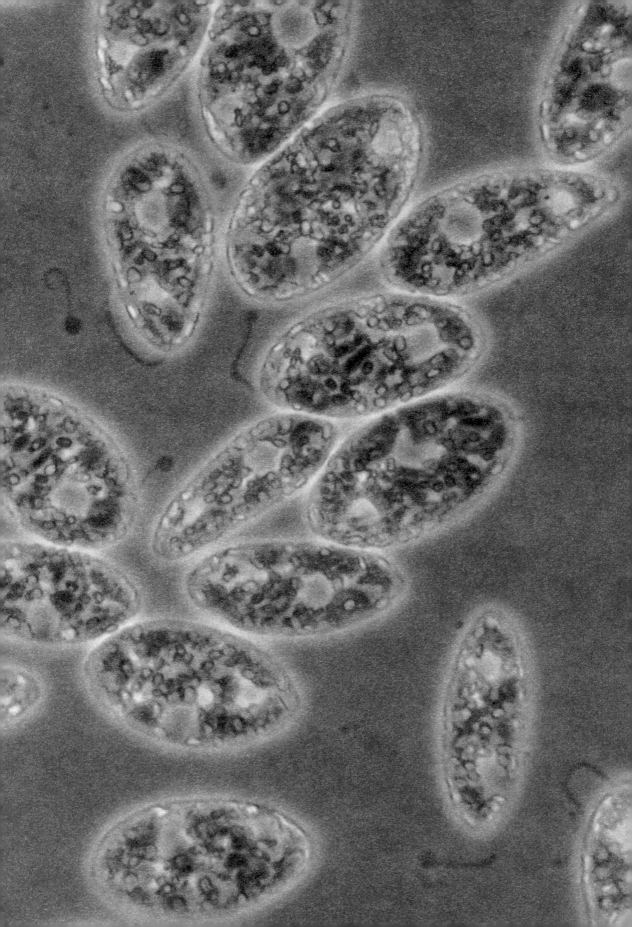

THE
EVIDENCE
OF
EVOLUTION

by NICHOLAS HOTTON III

Consultants

FRANCIS HUEBER
Curator in Charge, Paleobotany

RICHARD BENSON
Associate Curator, Invertebrate Paleontology

CLAYTON RAY
Associate Curator, Fossil Mammals

Published by **AMERICAN HERITAGE PUBLISHING CO., INC.**
in association with **THE SMITHSONIAN INSTITUTION**

Book trade and institutional distribution by
D. VAN NOSTRAND COMPANY INC.

FRONT COVER: *a fossil skeleton of* Seymouria *(about two feet long), which has traits of both amphibians and reptiles and suggests a link between them.* FRONTISPIECE: Euglena gracilis, *a microscopic, single-celled organism of the kingdom Protista, shown in a photomicrograph. Embodying both plant and animal traits, the early Protista represent a stage from which both kingdoms might have derived.* BELOW: Dimetrodon, *a primitive, crocodile-sized reptile which lived some 250 million years ago. A savage carnivore,* Dimetrodon *is an early member of a line that evolved ultimately into mammals.*

CONTENTS

OF TIME
AND
CHANGE

The entire history of man, it has been said, could be summed up in one single phrase: "When do we eat?" But to limit such an insight to the career of one two-legged organism, however high our opinion of him may be, seems shortsighted. For the history of all life on earth could as well be seen as one continuous and arduous quest for sustaining energy, and it has been principally as a means of succeeding in that quest, that life, over billions of years, has "evolved" from a microscopic bit of sea-borne jelly to more than 1.25 million different species ranging from asters to zebras, and including you and me.

For all life is a continuum; all living things, despite their awesome diversity, are related to each other. And evolution is the term we give to that process by which the structure of plants and animals changes with the passage of time, thus accounting for the continuum.

Modern evolutionary theory was first set forth in detail by an English naturalist named Charles Robert Darwin a little more than one hundred years ago. Since then evolutionary thought has played a prominent, and frequently controversial, role in changing man's view of his universe from a static one, in which he is the apex of nature, to one that is dynamic, in which he occupies a small and undoubtedly transient place. The idea, of course, runs counter to a great many deep-seated anthropocentric notions, today perhaps no less than in Darwin's time, as we witness ever more impressive demonstrations of man's mastery over nature. Man, it would seem, is unique.

Be that as it may, man is still the only scien-

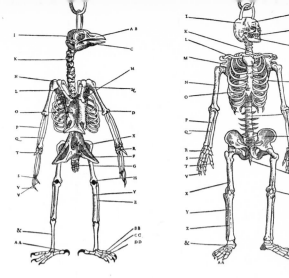

tist of whom we have evidence. And whether or not the objective universe has meaning in the traditional sense, man is the only entity who can trouble himself over such matters, and this at least chains him to a unique pinnacle on life's unfinished mountain.

Modern science relies on systems of logic and rigorous procedures of reasoning first developed by the Greeks and later revived during the Middle Ages. Unlike the Greeks, who considered external evidence of secondary importance to systems of thinking, the medieval thinkers concluded that external evidence provides the *only* valid grounds for the formulation of theory. And this new approach, which is still the heart of science, very soon led to important conclusions about the geologic history of the earth and about the origins of life.

In ancient times such phenomena as the appearance of frogs in great numbers following spring floods along the Nile and the appearance of maggots in decaying meat had given rise to the notion that under certain circumstances life could arise from nonliving matter. The concept (it became known as the theory of "spontaneous generation") obviously resulted from insufficient attention to external phenomena. Though the theory was generally discredited well before Darwin's time and does not figure significantly in the development of evolutionary concepts, its decline was essential to the advance of evolutionary thought. For as long as the idea of life springing forth on its own accord was taken seriously, a relationship of descent among life's many forms would not be considered.

An early step in the discrediting of the theory was taken in 1668 by an Italian physician named Francesco Redi. By allowing samples of meat to decay in two containers, one of which was covered with gauze to protect it from flies, Redi demonstrated that maggots developed only in the meat to which flies had access. His procedure was the controlled experiment, a technique invented to utilize external evidence more fully and objectively. The only conclusion he drew was that maggots did not arise spontaneously from dead matter (as was widely believed they could) but from tiny eggs deposited by flies. Redi did not attempt to take issue with the general theory, but subsequent investigation confirmed his work and served to demonstrate that spontaneous generation does not take place under present-day conditions.

In contrast to the development of the spontaneous generation theory stands the development of geology. The ancients were aware of most of the facts upon which modern geologic theory is built, but they never attempted to synthesize them into a comprehensive record. They knew, for example, that over extended periods of time sea levels rise and fall; that fossil sea shells on high land mark the former presence of the sea; that valleys are cut by the rivers that occupy them; and that rivers deposit large amounts of sediment in their lower depths and in the sea. For two thousand years these observations appeared and disappeared according to the temper of the times. Still, it was not until the beginning of the nineteenth century that they were incorporated by the Scottish geologists James Hutton and John Playfair into the modern geologic concept that "the present is the key to the past."

Meanwhile, the occurrence of fossil remains was being brought into modern perspective. Leonardo da Vinci, among his other accomplishments, observed that some fossil shells are found with their two halves "articulated" (in the position they occupied during life) while others are found with their halves disjointed, broken, and scattered, as though they had been moved about after death and before burial, presumably by the water in which they had lived. This established that fossil shells were deposited under a variety of circumstances and left doubts about their tie-in with the Flood.

Benoit de Maillet, a French consul in Egypt, recognized that stratification in rocks signifies a sequence in time, lower beds having been deposited before overlying beds. Further evidence of a time sequence lay in his observation that progressively lower beds contained fewer fossils similar to modern kinds of organisms. De Maillet's work was published posthumously in 1748, under the pseudonym *Telliamed* (his name spelled backward), perhaps in discreet recognition of the probable reaction of ecclesiastic authority to such outrageous doctrine.

Half a century later, in one of the great advances in the understanding of earth history, William Smith, an English surveyor and engineer, noted that successive levels of strata contained different fossil assemblages, which once having vanished, never reappeared. From his studies he developed the indispensable geologic tool of stratigraphic correlation, based on the assumption that rocks containing similar fossils are of approximately the same age. Accumulation of stratigraphic data on a world-wide basis over the past one hundred and seventy years reveals a history of life covering somewhat more than half a billion years.

Like geology, the discipline of comparative anatomy is based in part upon observations made in ancient times, rooted in the practical requirements of medicine. Anatomy, the chief objective basis of all medical study, was hampered during most of its history by a widespread prejudice against dissection of the human body. As a consequence, physicians were forced to approximate human anatomy from the dissection and examination of other animals. That the procedure worked as successfully as it did is a measure of the similarity of the animals studied. But it was not until human dissection became possible on a larger scale, as it grew more socially acceptable toward the end of the sixteenth century, that true comparative anatomy became possible, and this in turn produced about two hundred years of enthusiastic data-gathering.

Classification, or ordering of phenomena, is a primary requisite in the scientific study of anything. The Greeks were evidently the first to recognize this explicitly. But discriminating observation, upon which classification is based, is one process that man appears to perform almost automatically. In paintings on the walls of caves in France and Spain, which date back about twenty-five thousand years, extinct animals are depicted so accurately that they can be assigned to scientific categories erected by modern men on the basis of fossil bones.

CLASSIFICATION OF DOMESTIC CAT

Kingdom	Animalia	Eats food—self-propelling
Phylum	Chordata	Bilateral symmetry—notochord
Subphylum	Vertebrata	Backbone with spinal cord
Class	Mammalia	Warm-blooded, hair, mammary glands
Order	Carnivora	Flesh-eating mammals
Family	Felidae	Cats
Genus	Felis	Small cats
Species	Catus	Domesticated forms

Modern biologic classification stems from a system set forth by the Swedish botanist Carolus Linnaeus in 1737 in a book called *Systema Naturae*. Linnaeus' attitude reflects a preoccupation with external phenomena characteristic of his time. His expressed aim was convenience through logical order; he regarded his work as a catalogue of creation that would reduce the enormous complexity of the living world to a system in which parts could be studied piecemeal. The classification was in constant flux as new material came to light, even during his lifetime, and today few of his categories remain in their original arrangement.

But Linnaeus' system of categories and uniform method of naming plants and animals fulfilled his original aim of utility very well. We continue to use his convention of referring to each organism by two names, the first indicating the *genus* to which it belongs and the second the *species*. The domestic cat, for example, sports the scientific handle *Felis catus*. The generic name *Felis* signifies all small meat-eating animals with retractile claws and teeth of a distinctive character. The specific name *catus* serves to distinguish a group of varicolored animals with long tails that live with man from other kinds of *Felis*, such as the ocelot (*F. pardalis*), the puma (*F. concolor*), and others.

There are other cats that differ more from all species of *Felis* than any of the latter differ from each other. These differences are such that consensus among experts in classification places such animals in different genera, for example, *Panthera* (which includes the large cats: lion, tiger, leopard) and *Acinonyx* (leopard-

like but with claws that only slightly retract—as in the case of the cheetah).

The higher classification categories were set up after Linnaeus' time. Thus taxonomists now group *Felis*, *Panthera*, *Acinonyx*, and other sufficiently similar genera in a single *family*, designated Felidae, as distinguished from the family Canidae (all dogs), the family Ursidae (all bears), and about four other living families of meat eaters. As meat eaters, the members of all these families have many features of teeth and feet in common; they are grouped together in the next more inclusive category, the *order* Carnivora. The carnivores in turn are grouped with other orders of hairy, warm-blooded, live-bearing animals—such as the various hooved animals; the apes, monkeys, and men; and the rodents—in a still more inclusive category, the *class* Mammalia. The mammals, having an internal skeleton and backbone in common with the classes Aves (birds), Reptilia, Amphibia, and the four classes of fish, are included in the *subphylum* Vertebrata, part of the *phylum* Chordata. Finally, the vertebrates are included in the *kingdom* Animalia with all organisms that are motile (capable of voluntary movement) and heterotrophic (obtaining nourishment from outside sources)—in contrast to the generally nonmotile and autotrophic (self-nourishing) forms of the kingdom Plantae.

This classification is drastically oversimplified, but it illustrates the grouping of organisms in a hierarchy of increasingly inclusive categories on the basis of structural similarities and differences. Linnaeus was aware that within any species no two individuals, not even so-called identical twins, are exactly alike; but he adhered to the doctrine of "immutability" of species, the idea that species have not changed since they were created. Later in his career he suggested that perhaps species did vary with time, but his system remained in his view essentially nonevolutionary and static.

While the practicalities of Linnaeus' system were enjoying great popularity in biology, world-wide exploration kept turning up new forms of life, of which an appreciable portion tended to fall between categories instead of into one or another. And it soon became obvious that Linnaeus simply had not provided enough categories, with the result that we now have subphyla, superfamilies, and the like. This fact, coupled with increasing evidence of variability and of extinction, brought immutability of species into question and inclined some men to look at the Linnaean hierarchy as a continuum rather than as an arrangement of discrete units like books in a library.

By 1809, fifty years before the publication of *The Origin of Species*, Jean-Baptiste Pierre Antoine de Monet, a French naturalist who was better known as Chevalier de Lamarck, was treating classification as the documentation of a tendency of living things to evolve toward increasing complexity, subsequent to a single event of spontaneous generation in the distant past. He felt that the environment exercised a direct effect on the organism, arousing in it a "need" to which the organism responded by acquiring new characteristics through the "use and disuse" of parts. Over many generations the giraffe, for example, according to La-

marck's interpretation, would have acquired its long neck as a consequence of persistent stretching after tender leaves high on trees. He believed that if such acquired characteristics were maintained long enough in a given environment, succeeding generations would continue to exhibit them even though the conditions that had stimulated their development had changed. Lamarck's mechanisms have never been confirmed by close observation of specific cases. The concept of need, a central feature of his argument, was never clearly defined. His reasoning ran: An animal has a structure, therefore it must have needed it and acquired it because of the need.

Cuvier, a fellow countryman of Lamarck's, whose full name was Georges Léopold Chrétien Frédéric Dagobert Cuvier, established both comparative anatomy and vertebrate paleontology on a systematic basis. From such observations as the facts that mammals with grinding teeth have hooved feet and those with cutting or piercing teeth have clawed and padded feet, he developed the principle of "correspondence" of anatomical parts, the grouping of all animals with similar body planes into a phylum, all of which has proved indispensable in restoring the often scattered remains of fossil vertebrates.

Cuvier was a vigorous opponent of Lamarck's views, and he attacked his theories on the basis of the fossil record, which he maintained did not support Lamarck's idea of evolution from the simple to the complex. Cuvier pointed out, for example, that the fossil fish of the distant past could not by any criterion of the time be called simpler than those living today, and that the assemblages of fossil reptiles and mammals, which were then first coming to light, were more complex than those of his own time.

Cuvier remained a staunch antievolutionist throughout his long, productive career and believed that the characteristics of individual species were immutable, incapable of change. He attributed the extinction of past forms of life to periodic catastrophic upheavals, of which the Biblical deluge was only the latest. He believed that after each of these catastrophes the earth was repopulated from unaffected areas, or by fresh creations.

While this controversy was going on, comparative anatomy was being expanded by other investigators (among whom the German anatomist Karl Ernst von Baer is most prominent) to include vertebrate embryology, a discipline peculiarly engaging to the imagination because of its dynamic qualities. It embodied a process with a beginning and a culmination in which temporally distinct stages could be noted and studied. The developing embryo of advanced vertebrates, such as mammals and birds, goes through stages which, in succession, are closely comparable to embryonic stages of fish, amphibians, and reptiles.

For example, perforations separated by bars of cartilage and lined with mucous membrane develop in the region behind the head in all animals. In fish and amphibians these structures become functional gills and gill slits before the animal leaves the egg. In reptiles, birds, and mammals some of the gill slits disappear before birth, while others are rearranged into quite different structures, such as the thyroid gland and skeletal elements supporting the tongue. Similarly, a blind sac branches from the developing pharynx in nearly all vertebrates; in fish it either disappears or becomes the air bladder, an organ for control of buoyancy; in other vertebrates it gives rise to functional lungs. Since embryonic development, like evolution, is a process of change of form through time, its study inevitably gave comparative anatomy a strongly evolutionary slant.

The question of process and time was growing more significant in geology by the early nineteenth century, as it became evident that the Biblical span of six thousand years was not sufficient to account for the development of features on the earth's surface. In *Principles of Geology* (1830), the British geologist Charles Lyell summarized geologic evidence and concluded that processes currently active at the surface of the earth showed, in Hutton's words, "no vestige of a beginning and no prospect of an end." Lyell's work marked the birth of modern geology. On the basis of rates of deposition of sediments on large deltas and the wearing away of land along seashores and river courses, coupled with the tremendous thickness of sedimentary deposits of the past, he argued that present conditions must have existed on the earth's surface for millions rather than for thousands of years.

Lyell's estimate fell far short of present ideas concerning the age of the earth, but his concept, and the vastness of time it involved, exerted a profound influence upon Darwin when

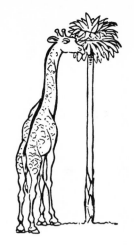

he was at a critical period in the formation of his views. In 1831, at the age of twenty-two, Darwin shipped as naturalist on the second exploratory voyage of H.M.S. *Beagle* and records that he first read *Principles of Geology* while tiding himself over a bout of seasickness that set in immediately after the ship left port. Lyell's work started him thinking in terms of biologic change at a slow rate by small steps. He notes, however, that it was not until the last year of the five-year voyage, when he observed the similarity between fossil and recent mammals in South America, that he was convinced of the truth of mutability of species. The voyage of the *Beagle* provided unprecedented opportunity for observing the diversity of life in many parts of the world, and his observations ultimately contributed an enormous documentation for his emerging ideas.

Darwin began his first notebook on "transmutation of species" in 1837, the year after his return. Well acquainted with the practices of animal breeders, who establish desirable characteristics in lines of domestic animals by deliberate selection of breeding stock, he felt that something close to the same principle must be at work in nature. But he was at a loss as to how it worked until 1838 when, by chance, he read a book that had been published forty years before—Thomas Malthus' *Essay on Population*. Malthus, who dealt with man from an economic viewpoint, asserted that populations tend to increase faster than their means of subsistence, and that unless checked they outgrow their food supply.

Darwin was struck by Malthus' phrase, "struggle for existence," describing conditions attendant upon overcrowding among humans. He noted that in fact most animals and plants produce more offspring than can survive under normal circumstances, and that organisms do tend to crowd their environments.

Darwin concluded that in a population living (as most do) close to the limitations of its environment, some individuals are better able to survive than others. "Can it, then, be thought improbable," he asked, "seeing that variations useful to man have undoubtedly occurred, that other variations useful in some way to each being in the great and complex battle of life, should occur in the course of many successive generations?" He reasoned that any "individuals" having any advantage, however slight, would have the best chance of surviving and procreating their kind. And conversely any variation that was the least bit injurious would be destroyed. "This preservation of favorable individual differences and variations, and the destruction of those which are injurious, I have called Natural Selection. . . ."

Those individuals that he characterized as "the fittest" were more likely to survive to reproductive age, more likely to leave offspring, and the advantages that permitted them to survive become increasingly prevalent in succeeding generations. Thus the long neck of the giraffe resulted not from continuous stretching, but because individuals with longer necks had a better chance of survival than those less favorably endowed. And thus chances were that long-necked giraffes would live longer and produce offspring with longer necks.

But, of course, the reproductive rate itself is a variable trait that may provide greater fitness for survival. If certain individuals reproduce more frequently or produce more progeny at one time, they contribute more heavily than others to succeeding generations, and a higher reproductive rate becomes characteristic of the population. A high reproductive rate becomes advantageous, for example, when the population is subject to constant attrition by flesh-eating animals.

Natural selection has been repeatedly confirmed since Darwin's time by experimental and field studies, of which a good illustration is the peppered moth. The wings of this animal are marked with an irregular pattern of black and white spots that blends well with the lichen-covered tree bark upon which the moth habitually rests. The English population of the peppered moth includes a melanistic, or solid black, variety, which was rare prior to the middle of the last century. As industry developed, soot from mills and furnaces blackened the resting places of the peppered moth; the melanistic variety became increasingly common, until now it is the speckled variety that is rare in industrial areas.

Experiments have demonstrated that the black moth is much more readily found and eaten by birds than the speckled kind, when it rests upon a background of speckled lichens, while the speckled variety suffers the same disadvantage against a black background. The melanistic moth is slightly more vigorous and has a greater reproductive potential than the speckled variety, but in preindustrial times this advantage was outweighed by vulnerability to predation.

It may be that melanism could persist during thousands of years of adverse selection only because of the greater general vigor of the black-colored insects. But the presence of melanistic forms, however few, was of great advantage to the moth population at large, for it permitted its survival in the face of a radical change of the environment.

Predation and starvation are sometimes savage checks to population increase, and they may provide a view of natural selection of diagrammatic simplicity. But they are seldom the most important. Populations of vertebrates do not ordinarily increase to the point of depletion of their food supply unless the environmental balance has been upset by a natural catastrophe such as fire, prolonged drought, or the activities of man. Fire, for example, may damage the food supply, as may drought; man may kill off the predators that ordinarily help keep the population in check. In other cases, however, the killing off of predators makes little difference in population size of prey animals. More subtle checks to population size, such as the defense of home grounds ("territoriality") and other aspects of sexual and social behavior, are now known to be at least as effective as predation and competition among species.

The concepts of the struggle for survival and of survival of the fittest have been widely misapprehended since Darwin's time, giving rise to what might be termed the fang-and-claw school of thought. This simplistic view, which has been utilized in certain political, economic,

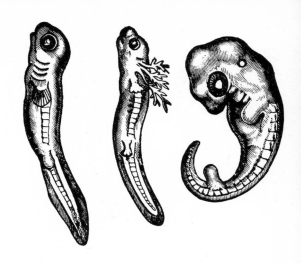

Among Darwin's champions was the German biologist Ernst Haeckel, who is known for the now-discarded "biogenetic law" that in the embryo an organism passes through a series of stages repeating the evolutionary history of its ancestry. These drawings, done in 1892 to illustrate Haeckel's theories, show quite accurately the resemblances among the embryoes of (from left to right) a fish, salamander, tortoise, bird, pig, ox, rabbit, and man.

and social contexts, bears little resemblance to Darwin's original statements or to the reality of the biologic world. Fitness does not necessarily mean greater strength, greater fleetness of foot, or greater ferocity. It is simply a description of the way an animal's characteristics, whatever they are, coincide with the limitations of its environment. Fitness is measured ultimately by survival of the species, not by survival of individuals. Furthermore, survival is not always a matter of competition. Group cooperation and various degrees of noncompetitive interdependence, both within and among species, determine fitness of populations, as was well known by Darwin.

In the exhaustive documentation of his analysis of evolution, Darwin drew upon the entire field of natural history as it was known in the early nineteenth century, and his thought exerted an immediate effect upon many of the fields by which it had been formerly influenced. In the case of comparative anatomy particularly, many of the embryologic relationships by which it acquired its evolutionary emphasis were demonstrated during the period that Darwin was active. In 1867 the evolutionary aspect of embryology was formalized by the German biologist Ernst Haeckel as the biogenetic law, or the law of recapitulation, which is epitomized in the statement, "Ontogeny recapitulates phylogeny"—embryonic development repeats the line of descent. Haeckel felt that the development of the embryo was a speeded-up rerun, in miniature, of the sequence of adult ancestors evolving over millions of years. His ideas were soon questioned and are now dis-

credited. The current view is that in its early embryonic development a living animal goes through the same stages as the embryo of any of its ancestors. Differences arise in later embryonic stages. The main trouble with Haeckel's theory is that he simply went beyond his evidence. The concept of recapitulation is useful so long as the conclusions drawn are kept very general. There is, for example, an obvious uniformity among all vertebrates in the development of jaws and gill arches in the embryo. But it would be foolish to compare the embryonic development of human arms with that of, say, the kangaroo's front legs.

Darwin's documentation of evolution—which is concerned more with processes than with sequences of evolution—consists of observations of geographic distribution, environmental relationships, and adaptations of organisms, many of which were made during the voyage of the *Beagle*. He also drew myriad details from observations made near his home in Kent, such as the citation of the interlocking chain of ecologic relationships of red clover.

Darwin pointed out that the only animals that pollinate red clover in Kent are bumblebees, and that bumblebee nests are preyed upon by field mice. The English keep cats, which prey upon field mice, and towns are concentrations of people. Therefore: the closer to town, the more people; the more people, the more cats; the more cats, the fewer field mice; the fewer field mice, the more bumblebees; the more bumblebees, the more red clover pollinated; the more red clover pollinated, the thicker it grows around towns in Kent.

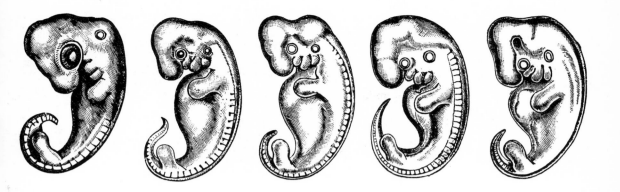

(Since Darwin's time, it has been suggested that the people who most commonly keep cats are spinsters; therefore, one should be able to tell the prevalence of spinsters in a town by the thickness of the stands of red clover around it. To my knowledge, the accuracy of this idea has never been tested scientifically.)

Although the theory of evolution by means of natural selection is customarily called Darwinism, exactly the same concept was arrived at independently by another investigator, Alfred Russel Wallace. He was fourteen years younger than Darwin, also had a strong background in natural history, had traveled widely in tropical lands, and, moreover, he had also been influenced by the ideas of Thomas Malthus. Unlike Darwin, Wallace took but two days to put down his theory in a manuscript, which he then sent on to Darwin for critical appraisal. Darwin read it while his own work was still in preparation, and his first impulse was to withdraw his claims in favor of Wallace. However, his friends Lyell and Joseph Hooker, a botanist, persuaded him to prepare a short summary of his work. Wallace willingly acknowledged Darwin's priority in the field. In 1858 their two papers were presented before the Linnaean Society in London.

The weakest point in Darwin's synthesis was that although variation was documented and was utilized as an objective fact, its cause was unknown. Darwin had no satisfactory explanation for the mechanism of inheritance. So, lacking any better idea, he leaned toward a Lamarckian view of inheritance of acquired characteristics, while recognizing its inade-

quacy at the same time. This lack was a source of concern throughout his career.

Unknown to Darwin, his problem was solved in 1865 when the mechanism of heredity was discovered by Gregor Johann Mendel, an Austrian monk, on the basis of experimental crossing of varieties of garden peas. The plants that Mendel worked with bred true for such characteristics as seed coat and flower color. He discovered that when a variety with wrinkled seed coats was crossed with a smooth-coated variety, the offspring resembled one parent only and not a blend of the two. When the progeny were crossed, both grandparental traits reappeared in their original form, according to rigid arithmetic ratios.

Because of his elegant planning, his experimental procedure, and his understanding of mathematics, Mendel concluded that the characteristics of his peas were produced by elements of unknown nature and transmitted by the reproductive cells of each plant. These elements are now called genes. The fact that in the progeny of the first mating the characteristics of only one parent appeared, he ascribed to the dominance of one kind of "gene" over the other; the characteristics which failed to appear in the first cross he called recessive.

Through a series of experiments Mendel established beyond question that physical traits were transmitted independently of each other, without change, from parent to offspring. And he went far enough to determine that development of some characteristics depended upon interaction of several genes. Mendel's work attracted very little attention and had no scien-

In 1858 an English naturalist, Alfred Russel Wallace (right), arrived independently at a theory of evolution almost exactly like that of Darwin. While lying ill in Malaya, Wallace had realized that natural selection was the key. In two months he had his theory organized and on paper and had sent it off to Darwin for comment. Darwin was flabbergasted and called the Wallace manuscript a perfect abstract of his own work, which was then still unpublished.

tific impact until it was rediscovered in 1900.

Among the early discoveries of twentieth-century genetics was the fact that genes are discrete particles which are subject to spontaneous changes, called mutations, that take place randomly at measurable rates. Their effects range from those so minor that they are detectable only by the most sophisticated techniques to those that produce morphologic or physiologic monstrosities incapable of survival. (The differences of flower color and of seed coat studied by Mendel had been caused by mutation in his stock at some time in the past.)

The discovery of mutations suggested that evolution might take place in a series of large jumps, as "lucky monsters" appeared that were fortuitously adapted to a different set of conditions than their parents. (To use the giraffe analogy once more, the long necks, according to the mutational theory, were the result of certain giraffes appearing suddenly, and just by chance, with a new kind of neck.) These ideas were soon abandoned, however, as it became clear that large mutations are in general deleterious, and that the odds against mutation producing a viable form significantly different from its parents are quite high.

Mendel discovered the principles of inheritance because he hit upon plants in which many characteristics were each modified by a single gene. The variability of these plants is consequently discontinuous, which means that crossing red-flowered plants with white-flowered plants produces only red- or white-flowered offspring, never pink. This contrasts sharply with the continuous variability of natural populations where crossing distinctly different individuals can result in a multitude of intermediate degrees, whether it is the color of a flower or the length of a mammal's tail. When mutational theories of evolution fell into disrepute, it appeared for a time that genetics had little relevance to evolutionary theory.

But it is now well known that most characteristics of wild animals result from the interaction of many genes, and that the vast majority of mutations cause only very small changes. As a consequence, when mutations first occur they seldom produce differences that are even noticeable. It is only after a multitude of mutations occur in a population that their accumulative effect becomes apparent. In a reproducing population the sum total of all genes, including their mutations, is known as the "gene pool." It is through the agency of sexual reproduction that the mutations present in the gene pool are combined at random to produce obvious new characteristics. These characteristics bring about small increments of change that are the building blocks of evolution.

However, relatively minor genetic mutations may occasionally produce changes that take place in big jumps. This happens when the embryonic development of one organ system in an animal (most often its reproductive system) is speeded up or slowed down. This phenomenon, heterochrony (literally, "other time"), is demonstrated beautifully in the development of the tiger salamander.

Most salamanders are fishlike before becoming sexually mature, and their sexual maturity occurs at that stage when they leave the water

for the land. Some tiger salamanders, however, reach their sexual maturity in the larval stage while still in the water. And as a result, in many cases, mature tiger salamanders never leave the water, but they remain essentially fishlike. In this instance, heterochrony could be said to produce regressive evolution.

Since the variation upon which organic evolution is based depends upon sexual reproduction, the theory of evolution depends ultimately upon the concept that all life stems from prior life. Following this argument to its logical conclusion, we are faced with the view that life has existed as long as matter has existed; if we find this untenable, we must consider how life did in fact arise from nonliving matter.

The fossil record does not help us resolve the problem. A few apparently organic structures are described from Precambrian rocks dating to about two billion years ago, but fossils first appear in abundance at the start of the Cambrian, in rocks about six hundred million years old, and these remains represent organisms of the same basic structure and complexity as many living today. Their complexity and diversity indicate that they must have had a long prior history of evolution, similar to those that gave rise to modern animals.

The relatively sudden appearance of fossils in the geologic record, therefore, does not mark the origin of life, but rather a time when a large variety of organisms acquired hard parts capable of preservation. Why this happened remains an intriguing problem.

However, two other lines of evidence, from geology and biochemistry, permit speculation about a possible origin of life from nonliving matter. Geochemical dating methods, based upon the presence of radioactive materials at a few places in the earth's crust, now permit estimates of absolute dates. Radioactive decay takes place at a constant rate, so that analysis of the ratio between certain radioactive elements and their breakdown products gives an estimate of time elapsed since the rocks containing them were deposited or emplaced. By this procedure the current estimate of the earth's age stands at about five billion years.

Geologic evidence supports a uniformitarian interpretation of conditions at the earth's surface back to about one and one-half or two billion years, but before that time conditions must have been very different. On the assumption that the earth was incandescent five billion years ago, its heat being supplied by radioactive decay, the dominant trend in its evolution is one of cooling. Allowing about a billion years for cooling from incandescence to darkness and for the formation of a solid crust, we have an interval, from approximately four billion to two billion years ago, in which to accommodate the origin of life.

As the crust solidified, internal heat caused volcanic activity, which must have been terribly intense. It is thought that the water that composes today's oceans was locked up chemically in the molten earth, and that it was first released as a gas, by volcanoes, thus making up the greater part of the primeval atmosphere. As cooling progressed, the point was reached at which water condensed at very high altitudes. Rain, falling from great heights, would evapo-

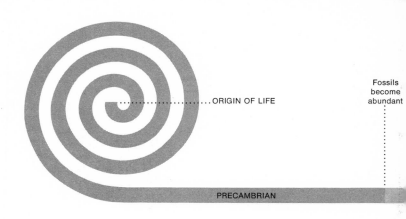

Though it is not known exactly how or when life originated in the "primeval soup" of the shallow seas, the fossil record provides a history of life beginning about three billion years ago, or roughly two billion years after the estimated beginning of the earth. The chart provides a comparative view of life's development. However, the line representing man's time on earth has been exaggerated in thickness in order to make it visible.

ORIGIN OF LIFE

Fossils become abundant

PRECAMBRIAN

rate because of surface heat, long before it reached the ground, to be recycled into the atmosphere. The level of free energy would have been extremely high: the atmosphere, being very hot, would have generated enormous amounts of static electricity from its incessant and turbulent motion; its inner layers would also have been subjected to intense bombardment of hard radiation from the sun, for there would have been no protective shell of ozone (a product of free oxygen, which was absent). At the same time, volcanoes were releasing large amounts of carbon dioxide, ammonia, and methane, which became the other major constituents of the primeval atmosphere.

These simple compounds consist of the same elements that make up the substance of life. Recent laboratory experiments have demonstrated that amino acids (a basis of proteins) and other vital organic constituents of living matter can be synthesized from these same compounds by subjecting them to high energy sources such as electrical discharges and ultraviolet radiation. These experiments were to duplicate the chemical compounds and levels of energy present at the surface of the earth.

Eventually, of course, the surface cooled sufficiently to permit water to accumulate in liquid form. As this stage was reached it must have rained continuously, literally for millions of years. The water filling the basins of the earth's surface must have been charged from the beginning with a wide assortment of complex organic molecules. It is estimated that the concentration of organic materials in these early seas, sometimes characterized as the "prime-

val soup," would have ranged from 0.1 to 1.0 per cent (in contrast to water as we know it in which the organic materials are measured in parts per million, rather than parts per hundred). In shallow and protected bays, where evaporation was faster, the concentration would have been even higher than 1.0 per cent.

For many more millions of years these compounds combined and interacted, and in shallow water the action was complicated by evaporation and by the presence of clays and salts, which cause the clumping of organic molecules. These clumps, just barely microscopic in size, are "coacervates." One of their characteristic tendencies is to gather into themselves simpler organic compounds of compatible nature. The formation of coacervates was random and was probably nearly balanced by comparable disintegration. Over the time span available, it was inevitable that combinations would appear fortuitously that were more stable or that could utilize simpler materials more effectively. Such chance combinations would increase in number and incorporate the simpler materials available and thereby cut down the opportunity for different kinds of combinations to arise.

The "life" of these coacervates depended upon an external energy source and supply of materials. But the continued cooling of the earth's surface brought about a crisis, for it reduced ambient heat as an energy source and drastically cut synthesis of simple organic compounds (amino acids) from inorganic materials. Those coacervates that depended upon ambient heat as an energy source or those that could only utilize simple materials found them-

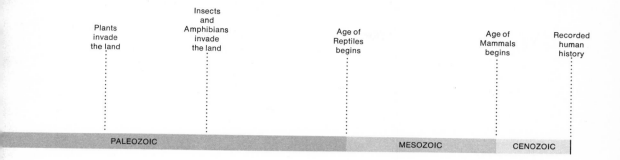

Plants invade the land | Insects and Amphibians invade the land | Age of Reptiles begins | Age of Mammals begins | Recorded human history

PALEOZOIC | MESOZOIC | CENOZOIC

selves at a distinct disadvantage. But those that could make use of chemical sources of energy and complex organic materials had the advantage and proliferated at the expense of the others. The net effect was to produce survivors increasingly similar to true organisms in terms of their "food-gathering" and energy-utilizing characteristics.

They were still a long way from being true organisms because their interaction with other organic material continued to be random and undifferentiated. If two coacervate globules combined into a single stable entity, the result might be more similar to one contributor than to the other, or it might be equally different from both. Was this process feeding or conjugation? At what point were large coacervate globules able to break into smaller ones, each similar to the parent globule? These questions cannot be answered at this point and are perhaps unanswerable. But with a billion years of random combinations in which advantages were conferred by increasing complexity, it is not surprising that definitive features of living organisms, such as a cell membrane and the cycle of recombination that we call reproduction, should have appeared.

A late stage in this process is related to the energy crisis; certain coacervate combinations occurred in which ultraviolet and other wave lengths of light could be utilized as an energy source—which was a crude form of photosynthesis. The high energy level of light gave such quasi-organisms (which might be considered the forerunners of plants) an enormous advantage over the forms that had to rely upon the

much slower-acting and less readily accessible sources of chemical energy. They could utilize organic matter more easily and probably could also utilize inorganic compounds such as ammonia and carbon dioxide.

A side effect of photosynthesis is the production of oxygen. As photosynthetic quasi-organisms became abundant, free oxygen began to build up in the environment—which, it might be said, was the great-granddaddy of all air pollutants. For it put into the atmosphere a gas that was highly poisonous to most organic molecules, and thus precipitated a final crisis in the origin of life.

The survivors of this crisis were the quasi-organisms that tolerated the poisonous atmosphere long enough to evolve a means of utilizing oxygen in a new kind of energy cycle. These forms gave rise, in time, to true organisms, presumably as the abundance of free oxygen increased to levels approaching the present.

The main reason for setting forth this kind of conjecture is to illustrate a plausible mechanistic explanation of the origin of life from inorganic matter, based, however tenuously, upon objective evidence. We need not concern ourselves further with the origin of life, inasmuch as the processes of organic evolution are applicable only to life as we know it. In spite of their diversity, living forms have a number of common traits that are not shared with the ingredients of the primeval soup, such as sexual reproduction, metabolic processes of a wide but not unlimited variety, a degree of independence from their environment, and a susceptibility to death.

EVOLUTION
AS A
LIFE PROCESS

Darwin and Wallace made the first clear statements that there are two distinct and complementary lines of evidence for evolution. One is the interaction of living individuals with each other and with their environment. The other is the fossil record.

Only in living, breeding populations of organisms can the processes of evolution be examined. But because the time at our disposal is so short relative to the time required for evolutionary change, study of evolutionary processes in living organisms is severely limited. And although the fossil record provides access to the time dimension of life—because it documents evolution as an enormously long sequence of past events—we can learn relatively little about processes from fossils, since fossils are dead and the record they have left us is incomplete. In order to gain a comprehensive understanding of evolution, therefore, it is necessary to work back and forth between the living world and the fossil record.

The basic principle of evolution is biologic change. At any point in time, then, any given group of organisms is in the process of evolving, rapidly or slowly, into one or several other groups. The present is merely one of an infinity of such points in time. The diversity of kinds, now or at a point in the past, is the product of prior evolution, and the variability of each kind is the basis of evolution still to come. An understanding of evolutionary processes begins, therefore, with an understanding of diversity. It begins with the comparison of similarities and differences among individuals that represent kinds and with the study of the var-

A pack of wolves feasting on caribou are caught close up by a telescopic lens.

iability of populations, their reproductive patterns, and their distribution.

Before we can discuss any aspect of the evolution of one kind of organism into another, we must first be able to express precisely what we mean by "kind." For this purpose we use the formalized taxonomic system (founded by Linnaeus) of describing, naming, and classifying organisms.

At the heart of the system is our nonscientific, ingrained awareness of the immense diversity of life and our habit of differentiating various kinds of living creatures by such commonplace terms as "alley cat," "bullfrog," "cockroach," "oak tree," and so forth. It appears that the closer the relationship between a human society and its natural environment, the finer the traditional distinction of kinds. In Hawaii, for example, four kinds of limpet—a marine snail—are now distinguished by separate names on the basis of taste, texture, and the environments they inhabit. Until recently, when the Hawaiian natives made this distinction, these limpets were all assigned by the zoologists to a single kind, but through the use of biochemical criteria it has been found that they do in fact represent four distinct kinds.

Our recognition of the reproductive nature of kinds is further reflected in such traditional expressions as "each after his own kind," "like begets like," and of the grouping of kinds by our speaking of alley cats and domestic dogs as beasts, of cockroaches and June bugs as insects, and then referring to beasts and insects collectively as animals in contrast to oak trees or roses as plants.

The essential difference between Linnaean taxonomy and the sort of informal taxonomy that is part of our everyday language is that the former is refined and standardized to deal uniformly with the entire living world. Of necessity it must describe groups of organisms in greater detail, define them more accurately, and express its conclusions in unambiguous terms. And to these ends it employs a highly conventionalized terminology, compounded of Latin or Greek roots, to avoid language differences and the semantic difficulties inherent in everyday terminology.

The basic elements of Linnaean taxonomy are species, which are populations of individuals that habitually mate only with one another. Species are categorized in increasingly more inclusive groups (genus, family, order, class, and so forth), so that each group above the level of species is an aggregate of species.

The taxonomic level at which we compare two populations depends upon the features being considered. For example, we separate the dog (*Canis familiaris*) from the gray wolf (*Canis lupus*) at the level of species by considering such superficial features as differences in coat color, call, and minor differences in bodily proportions. We can readily tell any dog from a wolf as they stand before us, but distinguishing between them by looking only at their teeth or feet is not so easy. The dental pattern and basic structure of limbs and feet are very similar in the two, and for this reason we place them together in a single genus, *Canis*.

The red fox (*Vulpes fulva*), on the other hand, is distinguishable from any dog or wolf not only on the basis of external characteristics, but also by marked differences of feet and teeth and other skeletal and muscular features. But if we compare feet, teeth, and general body build of a dog, a wolf, and a fox with the same features of a bear, we find that dog, wolf, and fox are more nearly similar to each other than any are to any bear. So we then assemble the doglike forms into the family Canidae, setting them off from the family Ursidae, which includes all the bears. Thus in the hierarchy from species to kingdom, at each higher level the groups become more inclusive as we consider progressively broader similarities.

A distinction, likewise, of the taxonomic level depends upon what features we consider. Just as dog and wolf are distinguished on the basis of superficial features, so we separate the leopard frog (*Rana pipiens*) from the bullfrog (*Rana catesbeiana*) at the level of species by such features as size, color pattern, and call. However, when we compare dogs and frogs as representatives of separate classes, Mammalia and Amphibia, we are up against an enormous complex of differences: the dog is hairy and warm-blooded while the frog is naked and cold-blooded; the female dog bears her young alive and nurses them with milk while the female frog lays eggs which she never sees hatch; the young of the dog are miniatures of the parent while the young of the frog look like fish; and so on in almost every aspect of the animals' being. And any of hundreds of species would show the same set of distinctions between the class Mammalia and the class Amphibia.

In these examples, the differences between species are superficial and correlate poorly with features of the environment. But when we distinguish between groups at any level above species, the characteristics that matter are those which fit the members of the group to an environment or mode of life. Such characteristics are said to be "adaptive." Any organism is an extremely complex mechanism fitted to the extremely complex business of surviving in its environment, and its features are functionally interrelated to that end. Adaptive change of one set of features unavoidably has an effect upon others, and the more strongly adaptive the change, the more extensively it affects the organism. The more strongly adaptive the features we consider, therefore, the higher the level of taxonomic distinction we make. (For example, the fins and gills of a fish, which are adaptive to life in the water, versus the legs and lungs of a reptile, which are adaptive to life on the land, separate these two major groups at the class level.)

Ultimately, however, each more inclusive taxonomic group is founded upon species. Though we may speak of the class Mammalia abstractly in terms of the features that its members have in common, when it comes to demonstrating those features we must pick up a cat or a rabbit or a mouse, each one a member of a species, as an example. We may talk about the differences between classes, but we must remember that the animals by which these differences are determined are also members of species.

Since species, in theory and most often in reality, are reproductively isolated, they should

also be characterized by their reproductive patterns. However, breeding patterns are exceedingly difficult to study in the wild and are known for only a very small proportion of living creatures. Of course, they are known for no fossil species at all, as fossil organisms have long since given up breeding. Because of such practical limitations, most species are therefore characterized solely by the physical features exhibited by individuals, and breeding patterns must be inferred—from physical variability and distribution of populations, interpreted in terms of genetic theory.

Similarities among the individuals of species exist because those individuals habitually breed with one another. At each breeding season genetic material is exchanged regularly, and when minor physical changes arise they are quickly diffused throughout the population. Consequently, differences between species are established and maintained by reproductive isolation. Since the members of one species do not normally mate with those of another, no genetic material is exchanged, and new features arising in either are not transmitted to the other.

Of course the awesome complexity of any organism's genetic background provides the potential for an enormous variety of minor changes that may be neither particularly advantageous nor disadvantageous under a given set of conditions. The primary effect of new features is to increase the variability of a population. But since genetic change is random, the odds against identical changes taking place in two isolated populations are extremely high; the randomness of change—sometimes referred to as *genetic drift*—causes genetic isolates to become increasingly distinct even in the absence of strong pressure of natural selection.

All members of a single species are brothers or sisters, parents or offspring, of other members of the population—even though this kinship may be a highly tenuous one. Their relationship is therefore the closest ordinarily dealt with in evolutionary studies. Genetic relationships between separate species can be approximated in the cases where their representatives, normally isolated in nature, are nevertheless capable of interbreeding in captivity. However, most distinct groups are incapable of interbreeding under any circumstances, and so determining relationships between them remains a matter of comparing physical similarities and differences.

In the process of evolution, as in the procedures of taxonomy, the species is basic because it is the only clearly defined assembly of reproducing individuals, and reproduction is essential to evolution.

Such familiar animals as wolves, men, bears, leopard frogs, and fruit flies provide evidence that new species arise from old when, and only when, small groups of individuals are prevented from mating with the rest of their kind.

The gray wolf (*Canis lupus*) and its close relatives the coyote (*C. latrans*) and the golden jackal (*C. aureus*) probably originated in the Northern Hemisphere, which contains the largest continuous blocks of terrestrial habitat in the world: the North Temperate forests and

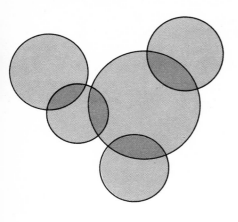

the vast, arid, treeless grasslands called prairies in North America and steppes in eastern Europe and Asia. The North Temperate forests form a belt stretching from Scandinavia across northern Europe and Siberia to the Bering Strait, whence, after an interruption of about fifty miles, they continue across Alaska and northern Canada to the Atlantic Coast. While the Bering Strait is at present an impassable barrier for most land vertebrates, there is good evidence that it has been bridged many times in the past, as the land rose locally or as the sea level subsided. In the New World, great tongues of forest extended southward east of the Mississippi and along the Rocky Mountain chain, and in the Old World through Germany and along the Ural Mountains.

The gray wolf originally inhabited all parts of this North Temperate forest belt. Variability of wolves in general is expressed in part by the existence of small, distinctly localized populations that differ from each other—much as species do—in such features as coat color, length of limbs, and size of ears and tail. But there are also wolves whose characteristics are intermediate between those of local populations, and through such individuals local populations grade imperceptibly from one to another, even between groups on opposite sides of the Bering Strait. There are no clear dividing lines between regionally variant groups, which as a consequence are regarded as subspecies of the highly variable species *Canis lupus*. A species in which regional variants can be readily recognized is said to be *polytypic*.

Regional variants of the gray wolf are the re-sult of partial reproductive isolation caused by the magnitude of the geographic area over which wolves are distributed. Although variability originates through random genetic changes, these changes are distributed uniformly only if mating is random with respect to the entire population. But in most groups mating is not random. Among wolves, as among men, individuals are far more likely to mate with their nearest neighbors than with animals that live farther away. In the gray wolf, habitual inbreeding among neighboring individuals produces local uniformity, but because of the phenomenon of genetic drift, no two separate local populations are ever exactly alike. This phenomenon thus ensures slightly divergent evolutionary trends, which may be enhanced to a further degree by slight differences of natural selection.

At the same time, the presence of intergrades—those animals that are the shades of gray between the black and white of different local populations—is evidence of routine interbreeding, whereby each group receives a continuous inflow of genetic material from the other. Reproductive isolation is therefore incomplete, and whatever distinctiveness there may be in the evolutionary trend of each population is continually being modified to a degree by some of the genes determining trends in other populations. Most of the local variants of *Canis lupus* probably have the potential of evolving into separate species if they should ever attain total reproductive isolation. But because they keep on modifying each other by genetic interchange, the breeding population that we can recognize as a species is the one that includes all of them.

The geography of their customary habitat has failed to completely isolate regional variants of *Canis lupus* because of three adaptive characteristics common to the entire species. First, wolves are big animals that travel long distances with ease (they can range forty miles a night). Second, within their range there are few environments in which they cannot thrive, human influences excepted. And third, wolves appear to exhibit little hostility toward strangers as far as breeding is concerned; they are, as every reader of Jack London knows, notoriously tolerant of the presence of dogs that have gone wild.

(The population of man, incidentally, shows several parallels with that of the wolf. Like the gray wolf, man is broadly distributed and exhibits marked regional differentiation. He is an even more tireless and adaptable traveler and is to an equal degree an eclectic breeder. Because of his greater mobility, there has been more extensive and continuous genetic exchange among adjoining populations, and, as a result, the differentiation of human variants has remained below the level of subspecies for at least the past ten thousand years.)

The coyote and jackal customarily inhabit more open country than does the gray wolf, the coyote being typical of the prairie, the jackal of the steppe. The clever and much-slandered coyote is distinguished from the wolf by its smaller size, lighter build, and wide repertoire of calls. These differences are not much greater than those that separate some subspecies of the gray wolf, but there are few or no intergrades between coyote and wolf where their ranges overlap, which indicates that reproductive isolation between them is complete. The coyote is therefore recognized as a distinct species.

The basis of reproductive isolation between coyote and wolf is no doubt partially geographic, but it apparently also involves behavior and habitat preference. In some animal groups, disturbance of the environment by human activity breaks down natural barriers and results in interbreeding between two species. This has not happened between *C. lupus* and *C. latrans*, in part because the former is forced out or killed off by man, while the latter thrives to a degree. Before the arrival of Europeans in the New World, it seems that coyotes avoided wooded country altogether, perhaps because they could not compete with wolves there. But with the retreat of wolves, coyotes are now frequently found as far east as Pennsylvania and New York, six or seven hundred miles from the nearest margin of the original prairie. Both species are persecuted equally by man, but coyotes get along despite these attentions. Being smaller helps, no doubt. But perhaps another advantage of the coyote is that he lacks the courage of the wolf. Where the wolf will make a stand and fight, the coyote will turn tail to live for another day.

It may well be that the massive destruction of timber that accompanies the advance of human settlement reduces the size of the forested range below the level that wolves can tolerate. Coyotes, being open-country animals to begin with, can then utilize both wooded and open

Red phase

Black phase

Cross phase

RED FOX

Blue phase

GRAY FOX

White phase

ARCTIC FOX

SWIFT FOX

COYOTE

GRAY WOLF

31

regional variants in such big animals as man and the gray wolf is even more effective among animals that are smaller, less mobile, and of more restricted habitat. In the eastern part of the United States the leopard frog occurs in a larger number of variants than the gray wolf does across half a planet. Contiguous populations of *R. pipiens* are connected by inter-

dom. The probability, therefore, is that the isolates in question will eventually become sexually incompatible.

This is evidently what has happened in some variants of the leopard frog, but since the populations that are incompatible with each other are still highly compatible with most variants, they are not complete outcasts from the gener-

*Unlike the wolf, which evolved
to inhabit areas of dense
forest, the coyote evolved
as a grasslands form, which
accounts in large part
for the coyote's more successful
adaptation to the presence of
that great wilderness conqueror,
man. As the map shows, coyotes
currently range over nearly
all of North America, even in*

Two traits of nature that greatly impressed Charles Darwin during his early studies were the capacity for variation and the capacity for procreation. Few living forms are better known for their reproductive talents than the rabbit, but as these photographs show, the Lagomorpha also demonstrate a marked range of variation and so serve as an excellent example for studying evolutionary adaptation to environment.

At upper left is the smallest of the rabbits, the tiny pika or cony, whose coloring and size are well suited to the crevices he inhabits in the rock slides of western mountains. To his right are young eastern cottontails, whose coloring and low profile fit in with the heavy brush, hedgerows, and weed patches they frequent. Below, at left, is the black-tailed jack rabbit, a superb example of a specialized adaptation. His long legs are designed for speed over the open spaces of his prairie or desert habitat. His elegant ears function as a heat-control accessory. (As a rule, hot-climate animals have larger, longer appendages to better dispel body heat.)

At right is the snowshoe rabbit, who is not only equipped with big back feet for swift maneuvering over deep snow, but to blend with his north-country home, he turns white in winter, and consequently is also known as the varying hare.

al leopard frog population and must still be considered part of it.

In rare cases genetic incompatibility may be the original cause of reproductive isolation. For example, it is known to have appeared in a species of South American fruit fly (*Drosophila melanogaster*) before any physical, physiological, or behavioral distinctiveness had been developed. Samples of this group can be distinguished from those of another only by the fact that, when they are crossed, no offspring appear. The populations are considered to be distinct species because in the last analysis they can be differentiated on the basis of reproductive physiology, and there certainly is no chance of gene exchange between them. Presumably, if both species do survive, random genetic recombination, possibly abetted by natural selection, will eventually bring about distinguishable physical differences.

Since the origin of genetic incompatibility is always a matter of chance, it is not an inevitable result of other forms of isolation; nor is it essential to the origin of new species. The separate species of *Canis* that we have examined are completely compatible, while on the other hand, some subspecies of *Rana pipiens* are incompatible with other subspecies. In general, isolation is established by external factors such as geography or habitat preference, with genetic incompatibility following—as chance dictates. If the coyote and wolf survive long enough, it is probable that instead of merging they will eventually become incompatible. This will have little effect upon their subsequent evolution, since at this point they have already ceased to interbreed to any significant extent.

However, genetic incompatibility can have a significant effect upon evolution if it becomes complete at a subspecific level. A polytypic species like the gray wolf probably evolves rapidly, because each of its subspecies shares the variations of all the other subspecies through interbreeding. Any subspecies that is cut off by the absolute isolation of genetic incompatibility is immediately deprived of the variation of the whole parent species and is restricted entirely to its own small store. Genetically the subspecies is left to its own devices, much in the same way as a group of mountain people might be cut off from a meaningful exchange with the rest of their countrymen, if after many generations of isolation they had developed a dialect that was no longer intelligible to anyone but themselves. The incompatible subgroup loses the potential of broader utilization of neighboring environments, although if it survives it may in time become more closely adapted to its own particular niche or area than would have been possible had its members continued more widespread interbreeding, again, much in the way a mountain people might become more closely adapted to their environment.

The differences by which we recognize separate species arise in animal populations in about the following sequence. First, near neighbors mate more frequently with one another than with outsiders, which results in a sort of reproductive parochialism, if not isolation. Then genetic drift gives such groups a dis-

The largest living carnivores are the bears, and the largest of the bears are the Kodiaks, the grizzlies (a formidable example of which is shown at left), and the polar bears. Kodiaks (the big brown bears) can grow to 8 feet in height and weigh up to 1,500 pounds; polar bears are about their equal. Studies indicate that polar bears, with all their specialized equipment for arctic survival, are an evolutionary offshoot of the brown bears.

tinctive local character. At the same time occasional outbreeding produces individuals of intermediate character. An end to outbreeding isolates local groups. Intergrades disappear and distinctiveness is further enhanced by more intense inbreeding. This is roughly the point at which we recognize distinct species. Reproductive isolation, often due simply to geography, becomes reinforced by behavioral and physiological changes and ultimately may be rendered absolute by genetic incompatibility, although many species are recognized which have not yet reached this state.

It should be noted that natural selection plays only a minor role in all this, which explains why the features by which we distinguish species are not obviously adaptive. Evolution to the level of species does not carry a particular population very far from its parent species.

In contrast, the evolution of polar bears (*Thalarctos maritimus*) from a brown bear stock (*Ursus arctos*) illustrates a case in which natural selection does play an active role in the segregation of a new population from an old one. In its major outlines the process is the same. It begins with a polytypic species, and the new group becomes distinct as it becomes reproductively isolated. But, as we shall see, selection pressure was more intense and produced a more general overhauling of the animals' structure, so that the new population must be recognized not only as a new species but also as a new genus.

Brown (or Kodiak) bears, like gray wolves, are big, foot-loose animals that are distributed around the world in the North Temperate forest belt. Their population is similarly made up of regional variants connected by individuals of intermediate character. In view of the continuity of range and the mobility of brown bears, it is probable that interbreeding is routine, and that variants are subspecies of a single polytypic species, *Ursus arctos*. Just as the gray wolf has a smaller, slimmer relative in North America, so the brown bear has his little cousin, the black bear. North American black bears have a more southerly and easterly distribution, and although ranges overlap in the Rocky Mountains, there appear to be no intergrades between the populations. The differences between the two are rather superficial, of no clear adaptive significance, and we distinguish the black bear only as *Ursus americanus*.

North of the forest belt, across the treeless arctic plain called the tundra, on the shores of the Arctic Ocean, lives the polar bear. His range does not ordinarily overlap that of the brown bear and his environment and habits are quite distinct. The brown bear dwells in forest and mountain and, like most bears, feeds promiscuously, mainly on vegetation, taking game and fish only on occasion. The polar bear may forage for vegetable material on land during the short arctic summer, but he is an expert fisherman and powerful swimmer who spends much time in the sea.

Although polar bears inhabit regions of permanent snow and ice, only the female hibernates, and then only in winter when the cubs are born. The male keeps going all winter long, roaming the ice floes and shelf ice in search of

In her stark, frozen world of drifting ice and leaden skies, a young female polar bear, estimated to weigh about 400 pounds, contemplates a photographer who dared venture within 150 feet of her for this rare portrait. An inhabitant of the Norwegian archipelago, she exhibits the special adaptive features of her species: white coloring, a streamlined head, and stiff bristles on the soles of her feet, which serve for insulation and traction.

food, which in such circumstances can only be meat—fish, seals, young walruses, and anything else, including man, that crosses his path. Polar bears travel enormous distances, and it is conceivable that during hard winters occasional strays may wander temporarily into southerly areas occupied by brown bears. Even should this happen, however, the two groups are kept from meeting by behavior patterns, for, unlike polar bears, both male and female brown bears hibernate, especially in the more northerly parts of their range.

As might be expected, the physical structure of polar bears is sharply different from that of brown bears, and many of the differences can be associated with differences in environment or habit. Most significant are the polar bear's teeth, which are modified extensively from the brown bear's in response to the predominantly carnivorous diet. Polar bears bulk as large as the largest brown bears (some weighing as much as half a ton, or more), but their necks and heads are longer and more streamlined, which may well be an adaptation for the capture of prey while swimming. Their eyesight is much better than that of other bears. Their coats are white and so serve as camouflage; and, finally, the soles of their feet are covered with stiff bristles for insulation and better traction on slick icy surfaces. In sum, these features are highly adaptive and involve more extensive change than the features by which species are customarily distinguished. We therefore separate polar bears from brown bears at the level of genus, under the name *Thalarctos maritimus*. (This name, which

means "sea bear of the sea," conveys one aspect of the polar bear's nature in no uncertain terms.)

Reproductive isolation between polar bears and brown bears is nearly as complete as external circumstances can make it, being ensured by distribution, ecology, and behavior; there is no evidence whatever of interbreeding in the wild. Yet in spite of their physical differences, polar bears and brown bears will mate in captivity and produce completely fertile offspring. This is certainly unequivocal evidence of close relationship, which indicates that generic separation may arise in a relatively short time if given a distinct enough environment and strong enough selection pressure.

Paleontologic evidence is sparse, but such as it is, indicates that polar bears originated in the Old World during the Pleistocene epoch, somewhat over ten thousand years ago, at the beginning of the latest advance of the glaciers. At that time the Eurasian continent supported a varied fauna of brown bears, including *Ursus arctos*, which probably consisted of a number of interbreeding geographic variants—as it does today. In southern Europe and Asia Minor, where climatic conditions were affected only slightly by the advance of an ice front, brown bears were little changed.

In the north, however, groups of brown bears were forced out or exterminated by bitter cold and shrinking food supplies, and what survivors there remained as small groups struggling for existence in an ever harsher environment. But since climates, no matter how cold (or hot), are often more tolerable near the

The ancestry of both bears and dogs (which means dogs, wolves, coyotes, foxes) can be traced back to a doglike animal that appeared before the end of the Eocene, some 40 million years ago. The first skull at right is of such an animal from a somewhat later time. The second is a Miocene intermediate between bears and dogs; the third, a true bear from the Pleistocene, exhibits the flat-crowned teeth suitable for the bear's more herbivorous diet.

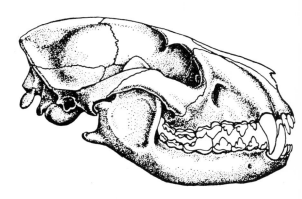

sea, it is very possible that some of these surviving brown bears made a desperate stand along northern seacoasts.

Here they became totally isolated by the migration or extinction of others of their kind in the interior. As food became even scarcer and conditions grew steadily worse, it was perhaps inevitable that these coastal bears would, on an increasing scale, turn to the sea for food. Some, of course, were better able than others to utilize the new marine environment. They were the ones who survived to reproduce, and in doing so transmitted the features that had proved successful to their offspring. And as conditions went from bad to worse, natural selection acted ever more strongly on succeeding generations, fitting them more and more closely to life in an arctic sea.

Polar bears finally became so well adapted to arctic conditions that when the glaciers retreated they had to move northward to survive. Perhaps as conditions improved in their European haunts, they found themselves unable to compete with returning brown bears, which, not having changed much, were better fitted to the now milder terrestrial environment.

It would be easy to get the impression that polar bears originated all in one "jump," owing to the scantiness of the fossil record, which in turn is partly the result of the polar bear's mode of evolution. Those survivors of the brown bear population that ultimately evolved into polar bears were no doubt relatively rare at any one time, so the odds against their having been preserved as fossils are correspondingly high. Evolution must have been rapid, but in theory, if we had a complete record of successive generations of Eurasian bears over the time that the change took place, we would have a series of animals that would be hard to distinguish from one another. Intermediate phases would not be very distinct from their immediate predecessors and successors. Even in a case such as the polar bear, where dramatic change takes place in a relatively short time, such change is the result of tiny increments of variation passed along from one generation to the next. The major difference between this evolution and differentiation only to the level of species is that strong selective pressure produces a larger number of more closely interrelated changes.

The differences between the bears and the dogs, like the differences between brown bears and polar bears, are the result of adaptation. But they are much more extensive differences and are more closely related to different modes of life than to different environments. The Canidae are more strongly carnivorous than any of the Ursidae, including *Thalarctos*, and their teeth are correspondingly modified for shearing, in contrast to the flat-crowned crushing teeth of bears. The dogs capture their prey by running it down and can maintain speed for long distances. In adaptation to this mode of life their limbs are long and slender, their first digits (toes) are reduced (the remaining ones are closely bound together by connective tissue), and they run and walk with the heel carried clear of the ground.

The lumbering bears, on the other hand, are

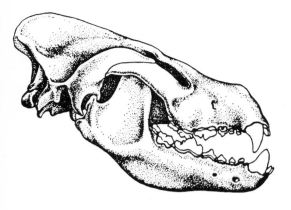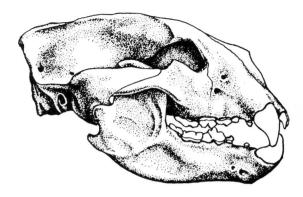

not well adapted to running, since normally they neither pursue prey nor are pursued. Their limbs are proportionally short and bulky, their toes are unreduced and rather splayed, and they walk flat-footed with the heel on the ground, even as you and I.

The first bears appeared in Miocene times, some thirteen million years ago, and are obviously derived from a stock that includes the ancestors of modern dogs. The members of this ancient group are sufficiently like living dogs to be included in the family Canidae; we say, therefore, that the Ursidae are derived from the Canidae. This is manifestly impossible, for it is not the family that reproduces, but individuals that we recognize as members of the family. However, we do not know which breeding populations within the Canidae gave rise to the bears we know today, and we can say only that all members of one family are descendants of some members of the other. To say that the Ursidae are derived from the Canidae is a shorthand means of designating this relationship. And the same principle is used at all taxonomic levels.

What we mean in terms of evolutionary processes is that at some time prior to twenty million years ago, a population (or perhaps several populations) that we would classify as species of dogs began to evolve toward a habit that was distinctive from that of other members of the Canidae. The new mode of life was so clear-cut and the diverging population became so thoroughly adapted to it, that we must distinguish the new group at the family level. There is little question that this evolu-

tion was of the same nature as the transition from brown bear to polar bear, but we do not know whether it was induced by environmental change of comparable magnitude or whether a large and varied population simply made the most of special opportunities in the overall environment.

The changing population could at any stage be classified as a species, and, as indicated by the variety of dogs and bearlike dogs preserved at intervals, was probably polytypic. Assuredly, the change required a considerable period of time, although we do not know how much. But during this period the more bearlike extremes were being selected for by their mode of life, and variants were in consequence becoming yet more bearlike. At the same time, other variants were being isolated more or less at random, thereby giving rise to distinct species. Some of these would no doubt evolve in a bearlike direction; others would remain as they were when they diverged from the main line; a few might evolve specializations of their own; and many would become extinct or would merge again with parent populations. A close look at a complete record—were there one—would reveal a tangled network of populations, including many dead ends (extinct creatures), stretching through time from a doglike to a bearlike animal, but at no point would there be a clear demarcation between the families.

Unfortunately (or perhaps fortunately, in the interest of order and sanity), the fossil record is never that complete, and in no case can we follow such a transition species by species. But when we consider a breeding population in

Turtles in one form or other have been thriving for something like 200 million years, and so offer a fitting subject for the study of evolution in both living forms and the fossil record. At left is the familiar box turtle; similar creatures have been crawling about for perhaps 70 million years. At right are the remains of Protostega, *a giant sea turtle from Kansas that measured over six feet and lived some 80 million years ago during the time of the dinosaurs.*

terms of its duration, we are faced with the conclusion that every species is part of an unbroken chain connected to its ancestors by a one-way genetic flow from past to present. The more closely related contemporary species are, the nearer in the past their common ancestry, and, in general, the more distant the present-day relationship, the more remote in time the ultimate point of convergence. In evolution, then, there is theoretically no point of discontinuity at which we can separate one species from another.

But the span of several human generations that we have at our disposal is nowhere near long enough for us to have made direct observation of genetic continuity in evolution. The span of time over which any species is represented by actual specimens, living or dead, is very short. In consequence, most living species do not in themselves show recognizable evolutionary change, though each one is a product of evolution up to the time at which we examine it. Nor do fossils provide us with much of a record of continuity of breeding populations. With few exceptions, the fossil record shows us only isolated segments of time, many of which are closely comparable to the present in terms of durations. Thus, although evolution emphasizes the genetic continuity of life, the material by which we study evolution is broken up into units: living animals are separated by reproductive isolation, and fossil animals by the incompleteness of the fossil record. In fact, so sparse is the fossil record, despite the tens of thousands of fossils that are stored and studied in museums, that to get a complete

picture of evolution is a little like trying to reconstruct *Gone with the Wind* from the scraps on the cutting-room floor. Although we may be able to deduce that the story takes place during the Civil War, that it is told from a southern point of view, and that it is centered in Atlanta, we might not be certain who the major characters are, let alone what the relationship was between Scarlett O'Hara and Rhett Butler. The one advantage the fossil record has over the scraps on the cutting-room floor is that we do know for certain the sequence in time in which things happened.

Therefore our procedure is to deduce the general course of the transitions by comparing the fossil remains at hand with examples of living forms. The fossils must, of course, have generic and specific names so that we can refer to them consistently.

Most paleontologic studies, especially of the older parts of the fossil record, deal broadly with the general pattern of evolution, not with the process itself. The process has probably been uniform for more than half a billion years, and it may reasonably be accepted as a postulate for broader studies. The general pattern, on the other hand, has varied continuously through time as some organisms have utilized divergent environments and modes of life and as their descendants have become more closely adapted to particular conditions. And it is the fossil record that provides the only documentation we have of such major adaptive shifts as the colonization of land, the origin of flight, or the advent of the warm-blooded ancestors of you and me.

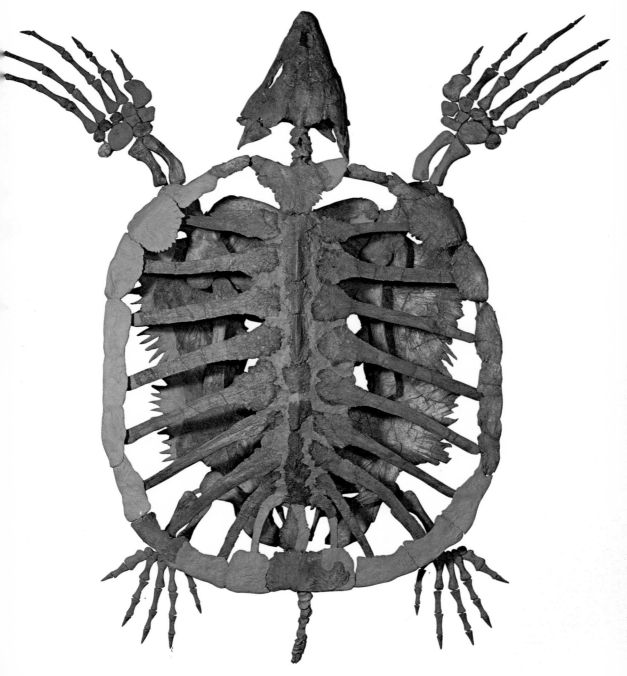

THE FOSSIL RECORD

All the evidence we have of the history of organic evolution is provided by the fossil record. But in order to understand what that record actually tells us, we must first consider how organisms are preserved as fossils and how they come to be discovered.

The fossilization of any organism is a rarity, but some stand a much better chance than others because of the environment in which they live, the geologic processes active in that environment during their lives, and the physical make-up of the organisms themselves. These factors all contribute to the character of the fossil record.

Long-term preservation and ultimate discovery, on the other hand, depend upon what happens to the beds in which fossils are preserved, subsequent to fossilization. Since geologic processes such as movements of the earth's crust, deposition, and erosion affect all beds without respect to the kinds of fossils they contain, the long-term preservation of fossils in any specific area is always a matter of chance. Fossils are discovered when they have been exposed, which is usually the result of erosion. But erosion also often destroys fossils, and consequently their discovery depends upon someone's being on the spot at just the right time between exposure and destruction.

The abundance, variety, and character of living organisms are determined ultimately by the physical conditions at the surface of the earth. Such conditions, of course, vary greatly from place to place and provide an enormous variety of environments of life. In the fossil record, however, we deal with environments of preservation which may or may not correspond closely to environments of life. Because the geologic processes by which organisms are preserved obscure living environments, we must concern ourselves primarily with such broad categories as the continental shelf, deltas and lower reaches of large rivers, the deep sea, and upland areas.

The continental shelf is the underwater terrace that borders all continents from the tidal zone to a depth of about six hundred feet, beyond which the bottom drops off sharply to depths of two miles or more. Distances from shores to the edges of the continental shelf vary tremendously. The North American shelf extends about twenty miles off the Pacific Coast and about seventy-five miles off the Atlantic Coast, while the European continental shelf underlies the English Channel and the entire North Sea. The depth of water over the continental shelf, on the average, is optimal for the development of marine life. Irregularities of depth and shoreline, and of fresh-water supplies, sediments, and nutrients from the land, introduce a large variety of lesser environments because they affect temperature and salinity of the water, composition of bottom sediments, and food supply. It is because of the richness and variety of physical conditions along the shelf that the greatest concentration and variety of life is found there. This has been true since the origin of living things.

The waters of great rivers flowing into the sea over the continental shelf contribute to that environment chiefly by bringing nutrients and sediments from the land. In addition, the lower salinity of fresh water sharply reduces the variety of life found in a river, and the direction and velocity of the current "selects" for organisms that can fight it (crayfish, snails, salmon). The density of life at the mouths of rivers is usually similar to that of neighboring portions of the shelf. Differences between physical conditions on the shelf and in rivers proper are gradual, and life that is near the mouths of large rivers is often of transitional character.

Seaward of the continental shelf, in the open ocean and its depths, the faunas are distinguished by a limited number of highly adapted animals, those of the open sea (whales, marlins, jellyfish) being specialized for swimming or floating and those of the deep (the outlandish angler fish, the brittle star, and the "living fossil" mollusk *Neopilina*) equipped for getting along under conditions of extreme cold and darkness. In neither habitat are variety and abundance comparable to those of the shallow seas, and few faunas of these habitats are preserved in the fossil record.

The upland environment, as I have called it, includes all areas that are not so close to sea level as to be covered by water for a large part of the time. Actually, this category includes a variety of habitats distinguished by differences in elevation, rainfall, climate, and plant cover. It also includes bodies of fresh water such as upland lakes and rivers. But most of these habitats are not covered by water, as reflected by the fauna they support: animals that walk, run, climb, and in some cases fly, predominate over those that crawl or swim.

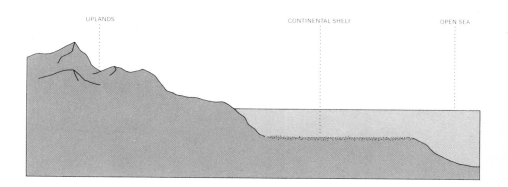

The physical features of all these environments include the geologic processes active in them. The rocks of upland areas are particularly subject to weathering and erosion because they are exposed to atmospheric gases and to alternate wetting and drying, cooling and heating, as seasons change and night follows day. By such means they are slowly reduced, ultimately to sand, clay, and lime, and these products in turn are picked up by running water—the sand and clay mechanically and the lime in solution—and transported by stages to the sea.

Generally speaking, the coarser material eroded from one spot is deposited again at no great distance. In areas of high elevation, however, deposits are eroded and transported again within a season or two. At progressively lower elevations temporary deposits are larger, last longer, and trap finer materials. Natural damming of watercourses may produce extensive local deposits of fine sand and clay that persist through several million years. But wherever the land lies at an appreciable distance above sea level, erosion predominates over deposition, and the general tendency is toward destruction and transportation of local sediments. Conversely, where the land lies near or below sea level, as in the lower reaches of large rivers and in shallow seas of the continental shelf, deposition predominates over erosion, and it is here that most of the finer sand and the clay accumulate.

Most of the lime is carried in solution to the sea, where it is deposited on the continental shelf by chemical precipitation from sea water or is incorporated into the body coverings of sea animals. For this reason marine deposits consist of sandstone or shale combined with limestone. In general, the purer sandstones and shales are laid down off river mouths and close to shore, while the limestones are laid down in clear water at some distance from shore.

In any environment living organisms are ultimately dependent upon the surface of the earth for the materials of which they are composed, and the bodies of all return to those surface layers when they die. Ordinarily animal and plant remains are destroyed without a trace as their components are consumed by scavengers and organisms of decay. Biologic decay, however, is arrested by burial, and organisms that die in a site of deposition, or whose remains are washed into such a site, stand a good chance of being buried under accumulating sediments. And since such hard structures as shells, bones, or woody tissues of plants are more resistant to decay than soft tissues, they are more likely to be buried before being completely destroyed. Thus the forms most likely to be preserved as fossils are those that have hard parts and live in or near the lower reaches of rivers or the continental shelf.

Only ten of the thirty phyla into which the animal kingdom is divided are characterized by hard structures, and it is these ten that compose the bulk of the fossil record. And all but one of the ten are present in Cambrian deposits and are the oldest well-preserved fossils, dating back about six hundred million years. As we have seen, the diversity and relatively sudden appearance of the Cambrian fauna have been interpreted to mean that hard parts

The Badlands are a prime example of a fossil-rich "upland" environment currently undergoing rapid erosion. Half again as big as the state of Connecticut, the Badlands were deposited by ancient slow-moving streams that wandered back and forth, leaving even layers of silt that are filled with the remains of mammals anywhere from 25 to 40 million years old: collie-sized horses, dogs, cats, and a huge rhinoceros-like animal called Brontotherium.

were acquired independently by a large variety of organisms in a relatively short time. Since the phyla of the earliest fossil record were already distinct by the time they acquired hard parts, the record of their diversification is lost forever.

The one exception, the phylum Chordata, was probably differentiated about one hundred million years after the first appearance in the record of other phyla. Very early in its history one of its subphyla, the Vertebrata, developed a characteristic bony skeleton that it has retained to the present. As a result, we can trace the general outline of chordate evolution, in the vertebrates, from a point much closer to the origin of the group than we can that of any other phylum, and we can follow it in considerable detail right down to the present.

The kind of information that can be derived from a study of hard parts (shells, teeth, bones) depends upon their relationship to soft tissues and differs widely among the animals preserved as fossils. In a clam or a snail, for example, the shell is a very simple structure with a limited number of muscle attachments and shows nothing at all about the nervous or circulatory systems. We can restore the soft parts of a clam or snail only by direct reference to living forms, and if the relationship of the fossil specimen is obscure, we may be unable to interpret it biologically with any degree of confidence.

The skeleton of a vertebrate, on the other hand, can be composed of more than two hundred elements, intricately jointed to permit a variety of motions, and the equally complex

muscular system can be restored from the marks of attachment that the muscles leave on nearly every bone. A complete skeleton permits accurate restoration of the general structure, no matter how bizarre or unfamiliar. Equally important, bones are physiologically very plastic, and in life are marked by the blood vessels, nerves, and organs of special sense that lie close to them. Some of the oldest known fishlike creatures, of unfamiliar but very well ossified structure, can be restored in anatomical detail comparable to that of most dissecting-room specimens.

Many invertebrates such as clams or snails are gregarious, sedentary dwellers in relatively still water, and so are quite likely to be preserved in numbers, in places comparable to those they occupied in life. The entire shape of such an animal, insofar as it is preserved as a fossil, is represented by one or two shells. It is therefore often possible to collect large numbers of individuals, and by measuring such features as width of shell or the position of muscle scars, to reach conclusions about their growth and variation.

Vertebrates, on the other hand, are generally considerably more active than clams or snails, and many inhabit flowing water. For them, getting about in life often means death in isolation, and parts of their skeletons, becoming disjointed as their bodies decay, are scattered abroad by currents. Under these circumstances it is impossible to recover any large proportion of the parts of a single individual. To find an articulated skeleton is a rare event. Moreover, contrary to popular opinion, we cannot restore

a complete skeleton "from a single toe-bone." Thus fossil remains of vertebrates seldom represent the numbers of complete individuals that invertebrate remains do, and only rarely can one deal with fossil vertebrates in terms of their populations.

The bones or shells of animals and leaves and twigs of plants share the fate of the surface upon which they come to rest. In upland areas the rapidity of weathering and predominance of erosion drastically reduce the upland dwellers' chances for preservation. More often than not, their skeletal remains are either completely destroyed by weathering or are battered to pieces by fast-running water. Burial in local upland deposits improves their chances only slightly, for the life expectancy of these deposits is short. Sooner or later they too are torn up by erosion, their contents scattered and destroyed.

Truly upland forms, in contrast to dwellers in pools and swamps along rivers, are therefore rare in all but relatively young deposits. In lowland areas, however, where the motion of water is generally slower and gentler, and deposition predominates over erosion, the chances of skeletal parts finding a final resting place are very much greater.

Still, even in lowlands, most fresh-water organisms live in flowing water, and the dwellers on the shores of rivers and seas must be washed into the water before they can be preserved. The remains of most fresh-water and land organisms thus arrive at their place of burial through the agency of flowing water, and so it is likely that the environment in which they

are preserved is quite different from that in which they lived.

Though the waters of the continental shelf are also affected by currents (from winds, tides, and incoming rivers), there are more areas on the shelf than elsewhere in which currents are negligible, and the remains of animals that live in these places are not transported but buried where they lived. In such cases, obviously, the environment of preservation corresponds closely to the environment of life.

The final stage in the preservation of fossils takes place after burial, as water seeping through the beds deposits a hard mineral such as lime or silica around organic remains and in the vacancies left by the decay of soft tissue. This process depends more upon the mineral content of the seeping water than it does upon the depth or duration of burial. The bones of mice or lizards deposited in caves no more than a few hundred years ago may be more heavily mineralized than those of dinosaurs deposited in sandstones a hundred million years ago. But in general, remains that have been deeply buried for a long time are heavily mineralized. Actually, the physics and chemistry of fossilization are still not thoroughly understood, but whether fossils are preserved or destroyed depends as much upon the physical factors of their burial sites as upon the biologic nature of the original organisms.

Low continental areas often mark a region where the crust of the earth is sinking slowly, while neighboring uplands mark a region of concomitant uplift. Limestones, as well as sands and clays, may be deposited if the

subsiding basin is very broad and lies below sea level and if the adjoining uplands are of low elevation. If the uplands are very high, deposition of sands and clays predominates over that of limestones. When the rate of sinking is matched by the rate of infilling, and the process continues for a long time, enormously thick beds of sandstone and shale accumulate. They are often highly fossiliferous, since the population density of organisms in such areas is nearly always high.

Sooner or later, however, subsidence of a basin comes to a halt and the area is uplifted; the erstwhile uplands may be lifted at the same time, or they may subside to sea level to become a basin of deposition. The old basin may be raised with little change in position of the beds, or with folding, as in the building of mountains such as the Alps or the Appalachians. In either case, the sediments that accumulated in the former basin are now exposed to weathering and erosion and are subsequently washed away to accumulate in new basins of deposition, while burying and fossilizing the remains of the inhabitants of those new basins. Since many of the upland rocks are themselves fossiliferous, the preservation of organisms in the new basins inevitably entails destruction of older fossils. Just such a process is now going on in the Badlands of South Dakota.

Throughout the history of the earth the continents have undergone repeated cycles of uplift and depression. In some areas the cycles are very slow. In such areas basins of deposition have persisted for periods of as long as several hundred million years; sediments accumulated in enormous thickness and the older beds were buried very deeply. But eventually, uplift followed subsidence; erosion predominated for a comparable period of time; and deeply buried sediments were again brought to the surface. Other areas have gone up and down like yo-yos, with periods of erosion and deposition alternating at intervals of tens of millions of years.

Under these conditions many deposits were partially destroyed during the shorter cycle of uplift. But in aggregate they accumulated in great thickness, burying the older beds so deeply that no uplift has raised them high enough for a long enough time to permit complete destruction by erosion. Such ancient deposits nearly always represent marine or lowland conditions, since contemporary upland environments were destroyed by the erosion that provided the sediments that formed or covered them.

More recent sediments also accumulate in sinking basins to record marine and lowland environments. However, the uplands that provide the sediments are still in existence. We can walk on them and examine the material in transit, without waiting for it to be dumped into a subsiding basin of deposition. (Such beds are to be found in the Rocky Mountains, for example, in the Uinta and Bridger basins in Wyoming.) It is in this material that true upland environments are preserved. Although the period of transit is short, geologically speaking, the cycle is so long that some of these deposits date back sixty million years.

An area the size of a continent naturally en-

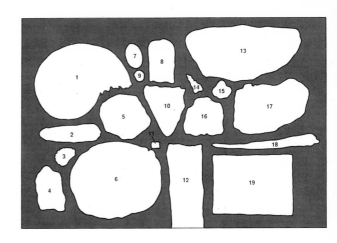

compasses a heterogeneous geologic history and is sculptured by complex and varied patterns of erosion. The fossil record that has been destroyed or remains buried in one place may very well be nicely preserved or exposed in another. On the larger continents it is possible to observe a comprehensive variety of environments of deposition and a fairly continuous history of life. But on no single continent can the entire history be observed. Such continuity as is available has been assembled from all over the world.

Limestones and marine shales representing numerous geologic periods are exposed over enormous areas of every continent. The fossils in these deposits are the remains of sea creatures (starfish, corals, and many kinds of shellfish), and their abundance and variety indicates that conditions of life were comparable to those of today on the continental shelf. On the basis of distribution of limestones and the faunas preserved in them, we may conclude that at different times in the past, seas covered large areas of the continents to not more than six hundred feet. (Such invasions by the sea did not require much crustal movement. If the sea level today were to rise about six hundred feet, for example, or if North America were to sink an equivalent amount, ocean waves would roll from New Orleans to Chicago, and the Appalachians would be a large island, cut off by a sea channel stretching from the Atlantic to Chicago via the St. Lawrence River and the Great Lakes.

Limestones and marine shales are best known in Europe and North America more because of the scientific orientation of their human inhabitants than because of any geologic bias of the areas. (In general, fossils are found where people are, and the more scientifically oriented, or curious, those people happen to be, the more fossils they find.) These deposits preserve the story of evolution of sea animals in a continental-shelf environment from the beginning of the Cambrian to the present, the full stretch of half a billion years. This is the most nearly continuous part of the record.

In north-central Texas and in parts of Oklahoma, Kansas, and New Mexico, pure limestone can be traced horizontally for several miles into beds of limy shale and ultimately into beds of shale and sandstone, a transition from a marine-shelf environment to the surface of a delta. The pure limestones and limy shales are evenly bedded and were deposited more or less steadily in water of fairly uniform depth. The shales and sandstones, by contrast, are often poorly bedded, and show ripple marks indicating shallow, flowing water and rain prints and mud cracks that are evidence of periodic exposure to air. The deposits of one season were exposed to air as flood waters receded, and surface impressions were left by occasional showers and baking sun. When the rainy season followed, the surface was again flooded by silt-laden river waters that gouged out channels in the low spots. But as the season waned and the waters lost velocity, mud and sand were dropped, the channels were filled, and the entire surface was covered by another layer of sediment.

Marine fossils in limestone and limy shale

are usually distributed in fairly uniform layers. By contrast, the fossils in deltaic shales and sandstones, primarily land and fresh-water vertebrates, are usually concentrated in small areas or "pockets" that are often associated with channels. The pockets represent small pools or eddies of still water along river courses, in which transported fragments of skeletons (and often leaves and twigs) were trapped.

The land animals of the delta (mostly turtle- to crocodile-sized reptiles) evidently lived and died along the watercourses in Permian times, their bones accumulating on land during the dry season. When the floods came, the bones were carried off until they drifted into slack water and were buried. Those partial or complete skeletons that turn up occasionally are the remains of the last animals to die during a particular season; their bodies had not been completely disjointed by the time the floods came. In a few places, the worn and fragmentary bones of land animals are found among the marine invertebrates of the limy shales, suggesting that the remains of the animals were carried out to sea, no doubt during unusually severe floods, since the distance they traveled must have been tens of miles.

In Kansas a complete skeleton of a land reptile measuring about six feet in length was found in a pure limestone. During the time the animal (*Ophiacodon*) lived, the nearest shore was some ninety miles to the east. Its burial in the limestone undoubtedly represents a rare set of coincidences by which the carcass was washed into a flooded river before decay had set in. The body floated, and so was carried west to the sea, even beyond the point where the river was depositing its finest sediments. It was still intact when it finally sank into the clear water of limestone deposition and was preserved in a purely marine environment, very different, indeed, from its original place of business.

The deltaic deposits of Texas and neighboring states were laid down in early Permian times, which was about two hundred and seventy million years ago. However, the channel-and-floodplain pattern of their deposits is characteristic of a variety of ages in other parts of North America, in Great Britain and Europe, Russia, China, India, South and East Africa, Brazil, and Argentina. Nearly all of our knowledge about Paleozoic and Mesozoic land and fresh-water life comes from this type of deposit, including such episodes as the earliest stages in vertebrate evolution, the origin of amphibians, reptiles, and mammals, and the evolution of the dinosaurs.

Such lowland deposits are smaller and less continuous than marine beds, and so it is often necessary to supplement gaps in the record of one continent with information from another. The early Permian animals of Texas, for example, are demonstrably related, on the basis of physical resemblance, to the late Permian fauna of South Africa, but there is no good late Permian record in the United States and no good early Permian record in South Africa. In Russia, however, the early part of the record is referable to the same age as some American deposits, and the late part to the South African

The first scientist to recognize the simple fact that different rock layers contain different kinds of fossils and that fossils are therefore the key to unraveling the earth's history, was a 19th-century English surveyor and field geologist named William Smith. "Strata Smith," as he became known, developed his system of stratigraphy while laying out canal routes; it is still used today in geology, archaeology, and paleontology.

deposits. Odd distribution of this sort is due entirely to geologic history, and not to any peculiarity of the faunas; very scrappy remains from Newfoundland indicate that animals similar to those of the late Permian and subsequent time in South Africa were also present in North America.

Though the margins of delta watercourses were almost certainly marshy, true swamp conditions are not well preserved in delta deposits. Such conditions are best preserved in association with coal deposits. These beds are marked by very fine-grained, uniform sediments that are black and tarry from the organic material preserved in them. They contain abundant plant fragments that include stems, seeds, and roots as well as leaves, and, in a few places in eastern North America and eastern Europe, they contain the skeletons of vertebrates, mostly amphibians and fish, which are usually complete and articulated. In rare specimens, even muscle patterns and the outline of viscera can be discerned.

Such quality of preservation is clear evidence that transportation was minimal and that the animals died and were buried where they had lived. Many of the coal swamp deposits and deltaic beds of the Paleozoic alternate with deposits of marine limestones, indicating that these areas were periodically invaded by the sea, as the elevation of the land moved up or down.

The environments of the uplands are usually preserved in far younger beds, which form a relatively thin veneer over the older deposits of the high prairie or steppe in the interior of every continent. Some of these beds, such as those of the White River series of the Badlands in South Dakota (which are of Oligocene age, or about thirty-six million years old), record a channel-and-floodplain environment similar in many respects to the Texas delta of Permian times. Like the Texas beds, they are marked by rain prints and mud cracks that record periodic exposure to air; but the White River beds are not associated with limestones or marine fossils, and appear to have been deposited in and near fresh-water lakes. They were laid down during a phase of deposition following the uplift of the nearby Rocky Mountains, but subsequent crustal movement has stopped the deposition and the White River beds are currently undergoing very rapid erosion.

Volcanic activity, which strews fine fragmentary material over broad areas, may also occasionally be the agent of preservation of upland environments. The Miocene period, about twenty million years ago, was a time of intense volcanism in the United States, and upland animals preserved by this process are found in many parts of the Great Plains and the Rocky Mountains. In a few places, falling ash trapped organisms where they lived, much in the same way that the eruption of Vesuvius entombed the inhabitants of Pompeii. But even as the ash fell it was subject to erosion, transportation, and redeposition by running water, and for this reason fossil occurrence in ash beds is similar to that of normal channel-and-floodplain deposition. And similar to the White River beds, these deposits are also being subjected to rapid erosion.

Upland environments are also often preserved in exposed terraces along the courses of large rivers, but the oldest of such beds cannot be older than the river valley in which it occurs. The oldest valleys of the Great Plains date back about thirteen million years, to the Pliocene period. The history of a river valley of that age includes periods of rapid erosion during times of increased rainfall or minor crustal movements, alternating with periods of infilling when the rate of water flow decreased. Material deposited in one cycle is not entirely destroyed by the following cycle of erosion, and so a sequence of events can be restored from a study of the terraces. (The Platte River in Nebraska offers a classic example.) Since such rivers flow across a generally upland terrain, the accumulation of fossils naturally provides samples of a good proportion of the upland animals.

When climates are dry, river valleys may act as traps for wind-blown dust, and animals are sometimes found buried where they had sought shelter from a dust storm in the lee of a bluff. Recently in a gravel pit in Fulton County, Kentucky, a bulldozer operator uncovered the fossil bones of four peccaries (wild pigs) buried in sediments composed of loess, a wind-blown silt. The animals had huddled together during a Pleistocene dust storm and were overwhelmed and smothered to death. They were found with their snouts pointing east, which may mean that the wind was out of the west.

Even more often the remains of upland animals are found in such natural traps as caves, bogs, and tar pits. In this country, Maryland's Cumberland Cave, the bogs of New York, Pennsylvania, and Michigan, and the La Brea tar pits near Los Angeles are among the best known. The pits of La Brea were pools of natural asphalt (oil modified by geologic processes) over which there was a thin skim of water. During the Pleistocene thousands of animals— saber-toothed tigers, mastodons, camels, horses, and numerous kinds of extinct birds— were caught in the asphalt when they came to drink, or as they tried to prey on animals already struggling in the deathtrap. Today, in the same area, animals are still caught in the same way.

But since caves, bogs, and tar pits are of very limited extent, it does not take much erosion to destroy them, and those that survive for us to study are seldom more than a few tens of thousands of years old. As a consequence, most fossils from caves, bogs, and tar pits are the remains of animals only lately extinct, or which may very well be still living in nearby areas.

But as much as fossil deposits depend on the right geologic conditions, their usefulness to science depends on human discovery. In this regard several kinds of rock have played a prominent role. The limestones in which marine fossils often occur frequently form prominent cliffs or ledges because they are more resistant to weathering and erosion than softer beds above and below them. Some sandstones that contain vertebrate remains are similarly resistant. Because of this some of the earliest discoveries of major fossil deposits resulted from the quarrying of such rock for buildings

and monuments. Similarly, fossil deposits associated with coal and iron came to light as a result of mining. Most of our knowledge of late Paleozoic plants, for instance, is based on specimens from the spoil heaps of coal mines. Digging into rock strata to build roads, canals, and railroads uncovered still other deposits. One hundred and fifty years ago, finds of this sort provided the impetus for the establishment of geology and paleontology as formal disciplines. (William Smith's work in the early nineteenth century, the very basis of stratigraphy, is the result of canal-building.) More recently, major fossil deposits have been discovered in the course of geologic reconnaissance and exploration by trained practitioners of those disciplines and by the world-wide hunt for that most characteristic fossil fuel of our age—oil.

A few very small deposits of fossils have been worked out shortly after their discovery, while others, which depended upon active commercial mining or quarrying for continued exposure, are no longer accessible because the mines or quarries are no longer being worked. But in general the larger deposits (the dinosaur beds of Wyoming and Colorado, the Tertiary deposits of the Rockies, the Permian and Triassic Karroo beds of South Africa) are so thick and are exposed over such a broad area that they are still productive, even though they have been exploited for about the past one hundred and fifty years. Furthermore, the exposure of the larger beds is continually renewed by erosion, so that paleontologists can return to them year after year, always with the assurance of finding additional material of scientific value.

The term fossil signifies, literally, "that which is dug up," which is true enough as long as we recognize erosion as the principal agency of exhumation. The popular notion that a paleontologist is a fellow who digs for bones is incorrect, for no paleontologist does any more digging than he absolutely has to. His primary activity in the field is to walk, looking for specimens that are being eroded out of the rock by creeks and rivers. The proportion of walking to digging is determined by the occurrence and size of the fossils being sought. Marine invertebrates are often so abundant in limestone that one can collect thousands of specimens simply by going to the nearest ledge, and by levering out, with wedge, sledge hammer, and crowbar, a few tons of material to take back to the laboratory. This technique of mass collecting, however, is not applicable in most cases to vertebrate fossils, because their concentrations are smaller and because they are, as we have seen, much more sparsely distributed. The absolute number of fossils in a thick deposit is great because the volume of rock containing them is so very great, but individuals and concentrations are scattered, and specimens must be collected individually, each one, as a rule, after miles of hiking. Vertebrates of all sizes are located by just this means, but while one can often collect small specimens merely by picking them up from the surface, collecting a dinosaur requires quarrying operations of respectable magnitude, quite often including the use of dynamite.

Two fossil skulls from the Smithsonian's collection illustrate the kind of problem that can puzzle scientists studying evolution. Both are the remains of Therapsida, carnivorous creatures that lived in South Africa about 200 million years ago. Officially, they are classified as reptiles; but they also have somewhat doglike teeth and other mammalian skeletal traits. At left, the smaller of the two, a cat-sized Thrinaxodon, has been reconstructed both as a mammal (those with hair) and a reptile (the earless, scale-covered creature at far left). Which way Thrinaxodon actually looked remains debatable, and because the fossil record of therapsids leaves no indication of skin texture or coloring, such details are strictly a matter of conjecture. But since there is solid evidence that mammals are in fact derived from reptiles, these animals represent what might be called a whole order of missing links.

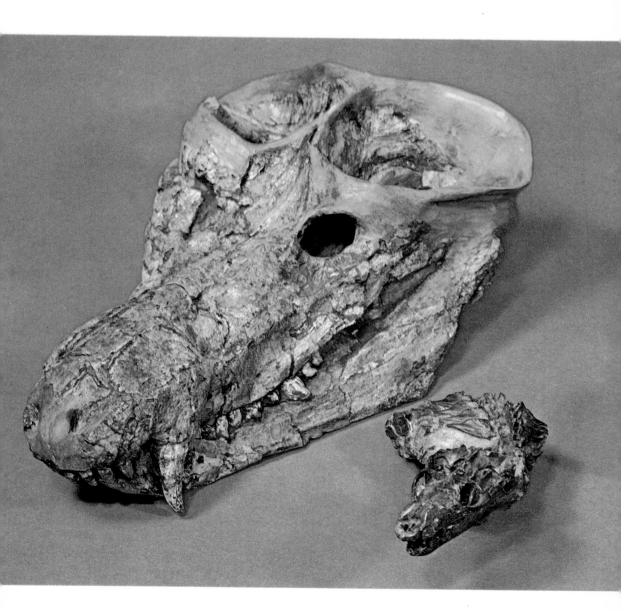

Since erosion destroys fossils about as fast as it exposes them, one of the disappointments a field man learns to live with is finding a beautiful skull that is too badly weathered to warrant keeping. The specimens that do find their way into collections are those that have been discovered in the critical time between initial exposure and disintegration. The length of that time varies, of course, according to the hardness of the rock and of the bones it contains. In many deposits of poorly consolidated material, if a specimen is missed during one season, by the next season there will not be enough of it left to be worth bothering with. In the very hard rocks of Texas and South Africa, on the other hand, if one collects half of a skull during one season, chances are that he will go back another season and get the other half. In one such case in South Africa, the elapsed time between the discovery of two halves of a single skull was on the order of forty years.

The size of a paleontologic expedition depends upon the size of the objective and upon the distance from supplies and shipping facilities. Most vertebrate fossils are relatively small, ranging from mouse to steer size, and nowadays there is a source of food and gasoline and a railroad station within fifty or sixty miles of most fossiliferous beds. As a consequence, the average present-day field trip is a relatively modest undertaking. Two men with a pickup truck, camping gear, and the necessary paraphernalia for the salvage of fossils in the field can manage very well under most circumstances—as long as one of them can cook. An experienced collector can even put in a profitable field season by himself, but because of the possibility of sprained ankles, snake bite, and other inconveniences, most parties consist of two or three men. All members of the party walk about looking for fossils, and all collect what they find. When the camp gets too cluttered for comfort, everybody takes a day off to go to the nearest town, where boxes are built and the collection is shipped back to the home institution. This is the dull phase of the work, but it has compensations in hot baths and air-conditioned motels.

The party may be a bit larger if it is after dinosaurs or whales, and such work requires far less walking and looking, and far more digging, packing, and shipping; but there is little more specialization of labor than in smaller projects. Occasionally, paleontologic expeditions that require cooks, mechanics, guides, and other specialists are fitted out to penetrate such remote areas as the Gobi Desert, but they are the exception rather than the rule.

We may, if we choose, regard the finding of a fossil as the convergence of two enormously long lines of coincidence. The simpler of these two lines has been reviewed in this chapter; in order for the fossil to be preserved and discovered, it must have included hard parts in its physical make-up, it must have been buried when it died, and it must have been exposed on the surface of the earth at the right time to intersect with the other line of coincidence. That other line is, of course, organic evolution itself, which has produced an organism that is capable of salvaging and interpreting the fossil and is willing to go to some lengths to do so.

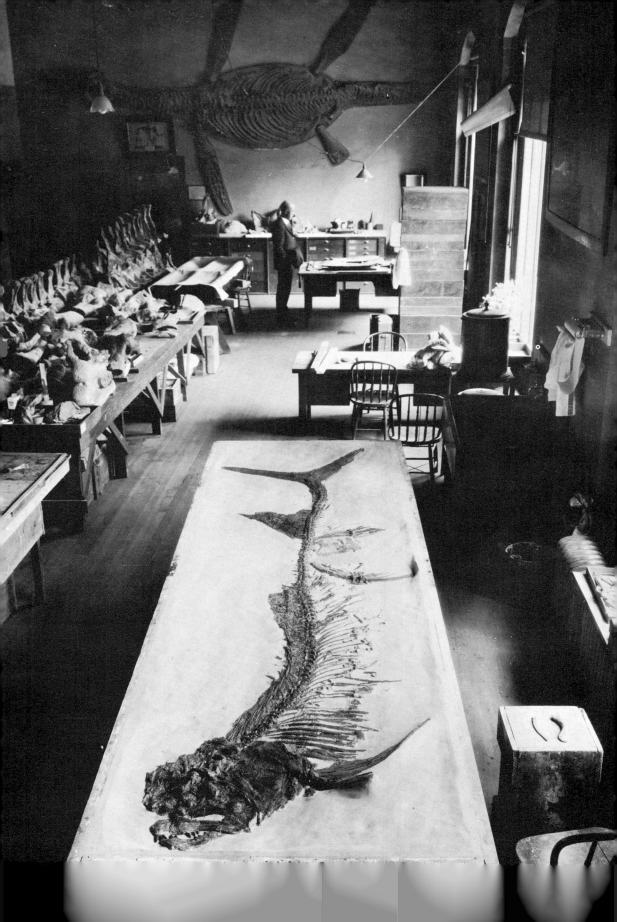

FROM THE
SEA TO
FRESH WATER

All the essential requirements of life, first met in the shallow seas about three billion years ago, are found today in similar marine environments along our continental shores. This means that life might very well have comfortably stayed where it was. And yet it did not. During the past five hundred million years, certain organisms have left the seas to thrive in progressively less congenial environments—first fresh water, then the land. Why they should have done so, when emigration raised problems they could have so easily avoided, is primarily a question of the opportunistic and expansive biologic responses of life. Any variation of the old environment offers opportunity—for more food, for increased living space, for reduced competition—and such variations have often led to new environments. Certain organisms have been able to utilize this opportunity by putting old equipment to remarkable new uses.

The invasion of fresh water from the sea may seem less consequential than subsequent moves onto the land, for both environments are aquatic. However, transition from fresh water posed problems as fundamental as any encountered later on land and sharply limited the kinds of organisms that could move out of the sea.

The substance of life is protoplasm (literally, "first-formed"), which in its composition and physical requirements reflects the physical features of the primeval sea. A colloidal fluid, protoplasm is mostly water that contains about the same proportions of dissolved inorganic salts as sea water. Elaborate molecules of proteins and nucleic acids are suspended in this salt solution, and interactions among them produce the physiologic processes of life. Because these processes take place only within a rather narrow range of concentration, protoplasm must be partially isolated from its surroundings in a package—the cell—the walls of which are permeable to water so that oxygen, nutrients, and metabolic wastes may be exchanged with the environments. The cell, therefore, must be continually bathed in water.

Sea water serves as a perfect extension of protoplasm, and the necessary exchange of materials requires little more than simple diffusion. But fresh water tends to enter the cell faster than it escapes, because of the higher salinity of protoplasm. This process is called osmosis. The unprotected cell takes up so much water that it soon ceases to function properly and ultimately bursts.

The functions of life involve a constant building up and breaking down of the organic constituents of protoplasm and require a continuous replenishment of energy and raw materials from the environment. How this process is carried out determines the primary subdivision of the living world into plants and animals. Through the process of photosynthesis all plants except fungi and most bacteria are able to convert the energy of sunlight into chemical energy. Animals and nonphotosynthetic plants cannot do this and so must feed on photosynthetic plants (or each other). All life, therefore, is ultimately dependent upon the photosynthetic ability of green plants. (And most of the photosynthesis so essential to

life goes on in the sea.) While plants, in and out of water, have tended to assume a sedentary mode of existence, because they can sit in one spot and manufacture their own food from materials around them, most animals have assumed an active mode, because they must go out and find their food supply.

But sea water is also vital to marine organisms for other than physiologic reasons. Protoplasm is highly sensitive to solar radiation of the intensity encountered at the surface of the earth; sea water reflects and absorbs such radiation. Protoplasm collapses without some kind of support; sea water buoys up the immersed organism with a force equal to the weight of the water displaced. And since all living organisms have a specific gravity that is little more than that of water, they "weigh" practically nothing when totally immersed.

The buoyant effect of water has given marine life two of its most characteristic features—the planktonic mode of existence and the sedentary mode as expressed in sea animals. Planktonic organisms are essentially passive, floating or swimming about weakly. Most planktonic plants (phytoplankton) are algae, which are nearly all photosynthetic and constitute the sea's basic food supply. Planktonic animals (zooplankton) feed upon the algae and upon each other, and in turn are food for larger animals.

The abundance of such planktonic life has made it possible for many sea animals to live a completely sedentary life, for they need do no more than sit in a favorable spot and feed upon planktonic organisms as they drift by. More-

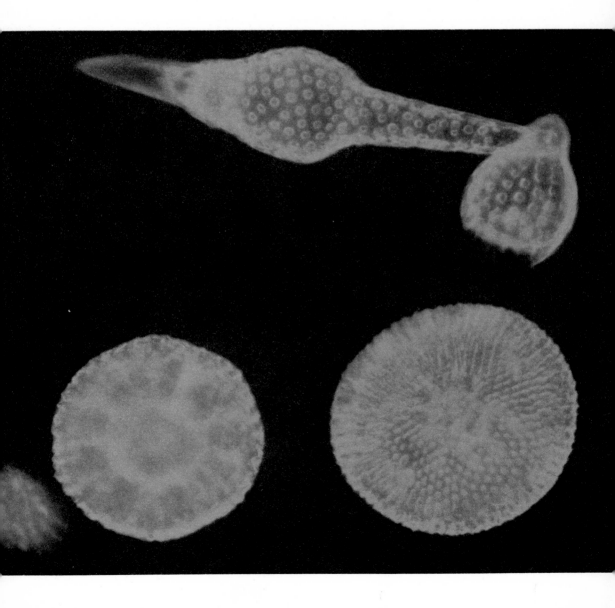

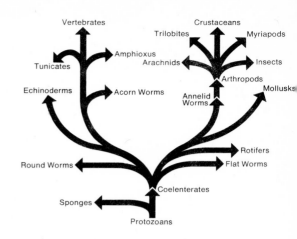

over, their mode of reproduction relies on the supportive effect of water; they merely release eggs and sperm directly into the water, which keeps the reproductive cells alive while providing a vehicle for their dispersal.

It is thus evident that marine life could have continued indefinitely without developing active locomotion or hard skeletal parts (external or internal). But such features had in fact evolved long before any organisms emigrated from the salt sea. The fossil record shows that active locomotion was nearly as common in the sea at the beginning of the Cambrian, six hundred million years ago, as it is today. Probably it had gotten started long before, at a time when life forms were becoming increasingly numerous and competition for living space was growing apace. Development of hard parts, on the other hand, dates back only to the beginning of the Cambrian and appears to be related to mode of life. Among such active forms as mollusks, arthropods (segmented and "leggy" invertebrates), and vertebrates, it is related to the mechanics of locomotion and feeding. Among such sedentary animals as corals, it is related to attachment to the bottom.

Fresh water differs primarily from sea water in the physiologic effect of its low salinity. But rivers, which comprise the bulk of the fresh-water environment, also differ from the marine environment in their constant seaward current and in being subject to severe fluctuations in volume and oxygen supply. So, not surprisingly, the predominant features of fresh-water animal life are active mobility and control over the osmotic uptake of water.

Physically the fresh-water environment is continuous with the sea by way of large rivers. Estuaries, or drowned river mouths, provide variants of the general marine environment. Upriver conditions grade from brackish to a completely fresh-water environment. At the other extreme, the shores of rivers and the ox-bow lakes, ponds, and marshes associated with them provide an enormous span of conditions intermediate between fresh water and land. Tidewaters, of course, are a more nearly direct route from sea to land, and the gradations are through time (as tidewaters rise and fall) rather than through space, as with rivers. As we shall see, a few organisms did come ashore by way of the tidal zone, but it appears that the vast majority utilized the river route, for the closest water-dwelling relatives and the most plausible fossil ancestors of most terrestrial organisms are fresh-water forms.

In the colonization of such uninhabited and erstwhile sterile areas as fresh-cooled lava fields or ponds on new volcanic islands, green plants must first be established before animals can gain a foothold, because of the dependence of all life upon green plants as the ultimate food source. This was as true hundreds of millions of years ago as it is today, and the first invasion of fresh water and land must have followed the same pattern—green plants first, then plant-eating animals.

Active animals had the physical capacity to penetrate all the way to the upper reaches of rivers; but before they could do so, the passive forms had to go there first, to provide a food supply. This the passive organisms could never have done on their own. But because of their small size, large numbers of them could have been carried long distances by waterspouts and violent storms capable of picking up tremendous quantities of water from the surface of the sea. Passive organisms could also have been introduced into fresh water through the cutting off of bays by offshore sand bars or by movements of the earth's crust; and, climate permitting, such bodies of water eventually would have become fresh. Storms capable of transporting small marine organisms over considerable distances and the cutting off of arms of the sea were no less frequent in the remote past than they have been recently, and they had more than a billion years in which to operate. So a majority of our smaller and less active fresh-water forms almost certainly are the descendants of organisms that left the salt sea in just such a fashion—not by preference, it should be noted, nor by any primeval inner drive to leave the sea, but because they were the victims of minor natural catastrophes.

Any organisms that survived a few generations in fresh water would have evolved a variety of adaptations to the new environment. In time a true fresh-water flora and fauna would have developed consisting mostly of algae and small animals, such as protozoans and rotifers (sac worms). And once the rivers contained a potential food supply, they became attractive to larger marine animals. But only those with an active and directed mode of locomotion could have taken advantage of the opportunities upriver, since only they were capable of overcoming the seaward current.

The locomotor system of such an animal is an elaborate complex of structures, requiring muscles for power, skeletal elements that serve as levers, sensory organs for guidance, and a nervous system to actuate the muscles and generally coordinate activity. The origin of such a system required more than the minor genetic changes that apparently produced tolerance of low salinity in passive organisms. It was the product of a long period of adaptation to active life in the sea that determined the character of a number of rather special kinds of creatures. The best examples of such creatures are members of the phylum Arthropoda ("jointed feet") and the subphylum Vertebrata, two groups that differ in all respects except in a marked ability to go where they please.

The locomotor apparatus of the arthropods is based upon jointed walking legs and a tough, light, external skeleton of jointed segments (made of chitin) which is shed and replaced at intervals as the animal grows. The central nervous system consists of paired nerve cords running the length of the belly, with concentrations of nerve tissues (ganglia) surrounding the alimentary tract just behind the mouth and others located in each segment. The head ganglia (roughly analogous to the vertebrate brain) receive sensory fibers from well-developed eyes, antennae, organs of balance, sensors of touch, taste, and smell and transmit motor fibers to the muscles of the jaws.

By contrast, the basic pattern of the vertebrates is adapted to swimming, for the earliest members of the group had no paired limbs of

The spider (second from right) and the scorpion (shown devouring a spider at far right) are familiar living arthropods, an ancient fossil of which (a trilobite) is at near right. Though often mistakenly thought of as insects, the spider and scorpion are characterized by winglessness, eight legs, and lack of antennae. The most successful phylum, the Arthropoda (jointed feet), includes more species than all the other phyla combined.

any kind. The skeleton is internal and consists of rigid bone; tough, rubbery cartilage; and, at some point in the animal's life cycle, a flexible rod of unique tissue called the notochord. The skeleton grows by accretion as the animal grows. The rigid elements are operated as a system of levers but are surrounded by the muscles that do the job. The muscles of the back and body wall are arranged in regular segments from head to tail. They contract in a series of waves passing from front to back, which throws the body into a succession of alternating S-curves, producing the swimming motion characteristic of fish. The central nervous system is a single hollow tube that lies along the back and is expanded into a brain at its front.

A uniquely vertebrate feature is the possession of gill slits, a series of small passages in the sides of the throat that are kept open by special bars of cartilage or bone. These passages function for feeding in early or archaic vertebrates and for breathing in all other forms.

The arthropods probably originated long before six hundred million years ago. They appear full-blown in the earliest fossil record and are well represented in marine beds from the Cambrian period on, but they have only a mediocre record in fresh-water deposits. The vertebrates, on the other hand, have left no record at all of their marine ancestors but are plentiful in fresh-water deposits after the end of the Ordovician period, or about four hundred and twenty-five million years ago. The arthropods therefore provide a better over-all view of their own transition from salt to fresh water, but the records of both groups are needed for a com-

prehensive picture of the colonization of fresh water.

The Arthropoda are divided into four subphyla, of which we shall concern ourselves with the Trilobita, the Chelicerata, and the Mandibulata. The trilobites, known only as fossils, are distinguished chiefly by what they lacked —specifically, biting mouth parts. (They evidently fed by plowing along the sea bottom ingesting small soft-bodied organisms and organic debris.) The chelicerates are best known by their living representatives: spiders, mites, scorpions, and the horseshoe crab. And the mandibulates include true crabs, lobsters, and shrimps; insects; and a host of tiny, less familiar creatures.

Prior to Ordovician times the trilobites, chelicerates, and mandibulates alike were strictly creatures of the sea, but only the trilobites remained so. By the end of the Ordovician, both chelicerates and mandibulates had found their way into fresh water. Since that time, in both numbers and diversity, mandibulates have become by all odds the most successful colonists of fresh water. (As we shall see shortly, they are also the most effective colonists of land, where as insects they are represented by about eight hundred thousand species, or about four times as many as in all other animal groups combined.)

There is no way of tracing the origin of the external skeleton and jointed limbs of the arthropods, for they are fully developed in the earliest fossil trilobites, which are the product of long evolutionary processes of which we have no record. There is no doubt, however,

that the arthropod skeleton was evolved in a marine environment, probably as an adaptation to the mechanical requirements of walking, which in turn was related to the peculiar mud-grubbing feeding habits of trilobite-like forms. Thus walking locomotion and the external skeleton were not especially contrived for fresh water. But once evolved, these remarkable features proved to be the key to the arthropods' repeated success in fresh water. In addition, their external skeleton was also, by coincidence, impervious to water diffusion and thereby helped to maintain water balance in the tissues. Together, these two potentials predisposed the arthropods to early and frequent invasion of fresh-water habitats. Such structures, which originate in response to certain conditions of one environment, but have the potential of serving widely different functions in new environments, are said to be "preadaptive."

Preadaptation, however, explains only those features that enabled the arthropods to immigrate to fresh water. It does not explain what caused them to do so. The answer to that is really quite simple: they were after food. As soon as small organisms became established in the rivers, certain mud-grubbing arthropods followed close behind. They encountered no competition and adapted rapidly to a diversity of fresh-water niches. In doing so, they diversified the biologic environment, and thereby provided incentive for still other forms to try fresh-water colonization.

Thus the arthropods literally walked into fresh water, attracted by food. Doubtless the first vertebrates (or their ancestors) were also lured by the same thing, for they too were mud-grubbers. But since our earliest record of them, dating to the late Ordovician, is from fresh-water deposits, we can only guess at how they got into fresh water by comparing the earliest fossil animals with their living relatives.

The earliest of the vertebrates are strange creatures to behold. They are fishlike, but they have no jaws and no fins. The skeleton of the head and most of the trunk consists of a single block of cartilage and bone that contains passages for the central nervous system, the alimentary tract, and the circulatory system. The throat region of the alimentary tract occupied the hollow undersurface of the head shield and was flanked by a row of solid gill bars projecting down from the shield. The floor of the throat is preserved as a mosaic of small scales and the fishlike tail by its covering of stout, closely articulated bony plates. The spinal column is cartilage instead of bone.

The Agnatha ("jawless ones," as they are known) were well represented during the Devonian by a variety of forms but were nearly all extinct by the end of the period. Today they are represented by the living lampreys and hagfish, which differ from their extremely ancient ancestors in having lost all trace of bone and in being parasitic as adults. Adult lampreys cling to fishes' flanks with their sucker-like mouths and rasp their way into their victims' bodies by means of horny teeth. Larval lampreys live in the mud of stream beds, feeding as did the early agnaths, drawing water in through the mouth and out through the gills.

Once passive sea animals and plants had established themselves in fresh water, more active predators followed very soon after in search of food. But unlike the tiny, passive forms, the new fresh-water colonists were able to make headway against river currents on their own accord, thanks to "preadaptive" skeletal structures and locomotive apparatus developed in the sea. The dominant predators were the arthropods and vertebrates. The arthropods (the formidable-looking lobster is a living descendant) fed by mud-grubbing and got about on legs. The vertebrates (like the modern-day golden shiners shown below) fed through gills, and later through jaws, and relied on fins and an S-curve swimming motion for locomotion. For both forms such features would later prove of immense importance when they began experimenting with opportunities in the more challenging terrestrial environment.

Three protagonists in the story of the evolving vertebrate ancestry are shown opposite. At near right is a very primitive jawless vertebrate known as Drepanaspis, *which dates from the early Devonian, or some 400 million years ago. Measuring about a foot in length, it was a bottom-dwelling filter-feeder that was capable of rather slow, clumsy swimming. To its right, at top, is a cross section of the larval stage of the tunicate, or sea squirt. Though in its adult form the tunicate is a sedentary spongelike creature, the immature form looks and behaves like a tiny, active fish. (The horizontal black lines indicate a dorsal nerve cord.) Below the tunicate is another primitive, fishlike bottom-dwelling chordate,* amphioxus, *shown as though dissected from the side. Amphioxus had no well-defined head and no skeleton, but because of the features indicated, it is considered a clear forerunner of the vertebrate fish.*

The fossil agnaths were small animals, few being over six inches long. The body of most kinds was rounded on top and flat on the bottom, like the shell of a turtle. Like arthropods they were bottom-dwelling mud-grubbers, but having no limbs they could not walk or crawl like arthropods, and their heavy head and trunk armor would have precluded any but the most clumsy tadpole-like swimming. Nearly sedentary, they merely shifted position from time to time by a vigorous wriggling of the tail. Some early agnaths, which had a more fishlike form, may have been somewhat better swimmers, but even these were covered by heavy armor and they must have been relatively sluggish.

The filter-feeding habit of larval lampreys and hagfish, and presumably of the early agnaths, is also characteristic of a number of other forms that are probably related to the vertebrates. We may therefore take a look at one further type of filter-feeder, the Tunicata or sea squirts. Adult tunicates are most unlikely looking candidates for vertebrate ancestors. They more closely resemble small sponges: they are sedentary; their bodies are encased in a tunic of cellulose-like material; and their circulatory and nervous systems are poorly developed. The body wall, however, consists mostly of an elaborate "gill basket," a structure comparable to the gill system of agnaths.

But it is the tunicate larval stage that completes the catalogue of basic vertebrate characteristics. The tunicate larva is an active swimmer that very much resembles a tiny tadpole. Its rounded head contains light- and gravity-sensitive organs together with a hollow ball of nerve tissue (a rudimentary brain). Its muscular tail is stiffened by a notochord, above which lies a hollow nerve cord that is continuous with the "brain."

During the first half of its short larval life the tunicate tadpole is attracted to light and repelled by gravity and so swims upward, where it is more likely to be moved about by currents (a device for disseminating the species). During the second half of its life its reactions are reversed so that it swims downward; landing on a suitable surface, it attaches itself and transforms into an adult. Because of its small size (about a sixteenth of an inch) the tadpole larva has no circulatory system, and because its larval life span is so short, it does not feed and has no digestive system.

The tunicate larva may be of great historic importance. The ancient marine agnaths (those older than our earliest fresh-water fossils) were undoubtedly not so sedentary as tunicates. Still, they were far less active than their descendants became. If the agnathid stage is regarded as intermediate between some unknown sedentary, filter-feeding ancestor that lived in the sea and a more active and predaceous fishlike vertebrate that lived in fresh water, then the little tunicate becomes a plausible "link" between the two. The critical change may have come about through heterochrony (the merging of larval and adult stages) some five hundred million years ago, at a time when a variety of organisms were beginning to enter fresh water. Retention of the tunicate larval tail—with its notochord and dor-

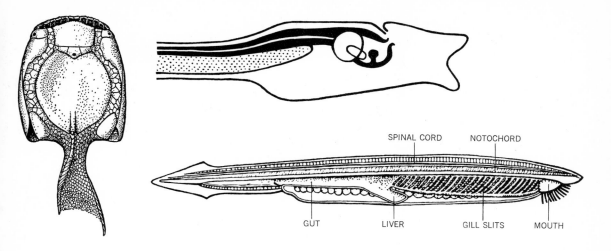

SPINAL CORD   NOTOCHORD

GUT   LIVER   GILL SLITS   MOUTH

sal nerve cord—by the filter-feeding and sexually mature adult tunicate would produce animals closely resembling the larvae of the living agnaths.

If these new animals retained the motility of the tunicate tadpole larva, they would also retain comparable sensory equipment, which would need little modification to steer them against currents. As this would cause the animals to seek out the mouths of rivers, guiding them toward a rich supply of food to which as filter-feeders they were already predisposed, such a reflex would be of great selective advantage—to the creatures that could tolerate fresh water, that is. (Those that could not would be knocked out, of course.) But with tolerance of fresh water and a current-fighting reflex arising at random, at any time the two might coincide. When that happened, our little protovertebrates would press promptly upstream. Eventually the development of bone would permit preservation after death, and the successful invaders would be immortalized in the fossil record as the earliest agnaths.

Although the vertebrates swam instead of walking, their swimming was of a sluggish, start-and-stop variety, an adjunct to mudgrubbing directly comparable to the walking crawl of arthropods, and similarly preadaptive to life in fresh water. It appears that none of the original colonists of fresh water were much as swimmers. The probable reason is that fast swimming is associated with a predaceous habit, and in the early stages, at least, rivers would simply not be as attractive to predators as to mud-grubbers.

A case in point is the class Cephalopoda of the phylum Mollusca. The cephalopods (octopus, squid, chambered nautilus, and many fossil forms) are extremely active, free-living creatures that have always been very successful in the sea. Their diversity of locomotive means is greater than that of any other group of sea animals. They can crawl on their arms; they can swim gently by means of membranes stretching between the arms; and they can swim with terrific speed and control by a form of jet propulsion, in which water is forced out of a narrow orifice of the body wall. Their general level of nervous organization is at least as high as that of arthropods. They reproduce by internal fertilization, and fossil members of the group are characterized by elaborate shells. Most of these features are as preadaptive as those of the arthropods, and so, theoretically, the cephalopods should have given the arthropods (and the early vertebrates) stiff competition in fresh water. Yet so far as we can tell, these remarkable animals have never approached the fresh-water environment at all.

That the cephalopods failed to venture afield is unquestionably explained by the fact that they were too successful as marine predators. Doing very well where they were, they had no incentive to go crawling up rivers.

Everything considered, no other groups of animals have been as successful in fresh water as the arthropods and vertebrates, but their closest rivals among multicellular animals are also characterized by a habit of directed locomotion, by some form of impervious covering, or, in one case, by high physiologic toler-

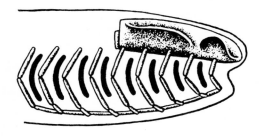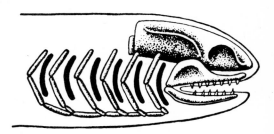

ance of fresh water. These phyla include the Mollusca (snails, mussels, clams), the Annelida (segmented worms), the Nematoda (eelworms, "vinegar eels"), and the Platyhelminthes (flatworms). Excepting the nematodes, which are predominantly fresh-water forms, they are all represented in marine as well as in fresh waters. The fossil record illustrates the marine origin of mollusks and annelids, and it is assumed that the others originated there also. In all of these phyla, except the nematodes, directed locomotion and control of water balance undoubtedly played a critical part in their entry into fresh water and thus can be regarded as preadaptive. This may also be true of the nematodes, but since they have no marine record we cannot make a firm claim.

Methods of fertilization also probably contributed to the success of each group in establishing itself in fresh water. Internal fertilization is characteristic of both fresh-water and marine snails and flatworms and may be regarded as preadaptive to life in fresh water. But in the mussels and annelids fertilization is external in marine forms and internal in fresh-water forms. In mussels, the difference involves only minor structural changes and may well have evolved in response to selection in the fresh-water environment.

Fresh-water annelids are quite different from marine forms in many respects, including mode of reproduction; and as they have no close relatives in the sea, we cannot guess whether their peculiar features arose in the sea or evolved in response to fresh-water conditions. Although very abundant in fresh water,

the mussels and annelids are each represented by a limited number of closely related kinds, and it appears that each group has invaded fresh water only once.

The most successful fresh-water colonists—arthropods, vertebrates, and mollusks—were all mud-grubbers to start with. As it happens, all three have a significant fossil record, and we know that they first entered fresh water nearly simultaneously, in the late Ordovician. The coincidence of feeding habit and entrance into fresh water suggests that establishment of a food source was the decisive factor in attracting them into the new environment. The phylum Mollusca seems to bear this out, for the mud-grubbing snails and mussels entered fresh water very early, while the swimming, predaceous Cephalopoda did not enter it at all, presumably because they found little to interest them in the food supply of rivers.

But though there is little evidence of predaceous animals entering the fresh-water environment as pioneers, the larger members of the fauna, especially arthropods and early vertebrates, provided a food source for predators, and in response to such opportunity some of the colonists soon assumed a more active and aggressive habit. The first among them were a group of huge, strange-looking chelicerate arthropods, Eurypterida, relatives of the living scorpions. Their limbs were modified for swimming, and in the Silurian period the eurypterids became the biggest arthropods on record, attaining a length of six feet. In some the front limbs became slender, grasping pincers. But for all their ferocious appearance, the

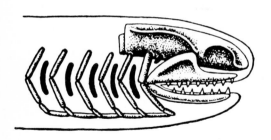

eurypterids did not last long. They declined sharply in the Devonian period as the vertebrates came into their own.

In the present day the largest, the most diversified, the most effective predators in fresh water or in the sea are the fish, as they have been for at least three hundred and fifty million years. The clumsy little jawless agnaths are most unprepossessing as ancestors of such animals, but the fossil record clearly outlines the stages by which they evolved to the estate of fish.

We know for certain that jaws, which became the hallmark of vertebrate predators, were derived from gill bars. In agnaths, the fifth of ten (or twelve) nerves coming directly from the brain can be traced to one of the front pairs of gill bars. In all living jawed vertebrates, the muscles that work the jaws are innervated by the same fifth cranial nerve. And furthermore, the jaws develop from the same embryonic tissue that gives rise to the gill bars, and all vertebrates go through an embryonic stage during which the jaws are indistinguishable from the gill bars that lie behind them.

Although the gills served primarily for filter-feeding and only secondarily for respiration in the earliest agnaths, it was probably their respiratory function that led to the transformation of an anterior pair of gill bars into jaws. As we have seen, the gill bars of the best known of these animals were solidly fixed to the head shield. Respiration could be carried on incidentally to feeding, agnath-fashion, only as long as the animals remained small. If they were to grow larger, the gill surface would be inade-

quate to supply the body's oxygen needs, for volume increases as the cube of linear dimension while surface increases only as the square. This problem could be resolved in three ways: the surface area of the gills could be increased disproportionately by folding or other complication; the rate of flow of water could be increased; or the gills could be made movable, which would certainly increase their contact with water.

The first two changes would involve only soft parts, and so we have no record of them, but some of the larger agnaths have gill bars that are movable. The increase in size with which gill-bar mobility was associated would also permit the animals to take on larger prey, which in turn would favor a manipulative function in the front gill bars. Once mobile gill bars became capable of handling prey, their conversion into grasping jaws would only be a short step. The respiratory gill bars of many fish are armed with tiny denticles composed of tissue much like that of teeth, and on those ancient bars that were converted into jaws, teeth evolved from just such denticles.

The earliest vertebrates with jaws belong to the class Placodermi, which appear in the fossil record some forty to fifty million years after the first appearance of the agnaths and which soon became predominant. The predaceous nature of the placoderms is reflected not only in their jaws but in their larger size and in their paired fins. Their success is reflected by their variety: some were small, swift, and sharklike; others were large and heavily armored, laying in wait for their prey on the bottom; and one

Unlike the Osteichthyes (the bony fish), which probably evolved in fresh water, the other group of "higher" fish, the Chondrichthyes (sharks and rays) probably originated in the sea and specialized for that environment. Streamlined, swift, and highly successful predators, the Chondrichthyes are known as the cartilaginous fish, since their skeletons are made of cartilage, not bone. The deadly looking specimen shown below is a sand shark.

group went back to bottom-living and mud-grubbing.

Paired fins arose (by steps unknown) in connection with the predatory habit because they provided stability in swimming. A fish swims in a straight line by swinging its tail symmetrically on either side of the body axis. If the tail is swung further to one side than to the other, the fish will turn in the direction of the longer stroke. But the asymmetrical stroke of the tail also causes the fish to roll on its long axis, in the opposite direction to which it is turning—thus it tends to bank the wrong way. Most fish counteract this effect by paired fins, which act as horizontal stabilizers. But a finless swimmer like a tadpole can turn only by maintaining contact with the bottom; if it tries to turn when clear of the bottom it rotates like a rifle bullet. (This is one reason why we believe that the finless agnaths were poor swimmers.

The paired fins of placoderms were simple membranes supported by stout bony spines. During Devonian times the two more advanced classes of fresh-water fishes, each with a refined fin system, arose from early placoderms and eventually replaced the placoderms just as the placoderms had replaced the agnaths. These two groups were the Chondrichthyes (sharks, rays, and others with a skeleton of cartilage instead of bone) and Osteichthyes (bony fish).

In the first sharks, the fins functioned as fixed keels but were stiffened by a skeleton of horny rays instead of a single spine. The first bony fish, which were contemporary with the first sharks during the middle Devonian (about three hundred and seventy million years ago) had ray-supported fins with a narrow attachment to the body that made them movable. They could be presented to the slip stream at variable angles, like the bow and stern planes of a submarine. As a consequence, such fish could now bank and roll as they pleased and execute far tighter maneuvers, a feature of great advantage to any swimmer. By using the mobile fins as paddles, they could back and fill as never before.

The sharks invaded the sea at the end of the Devonian and later developed narrow-based fins like those of bony fish, but not soon enough to prevent their near extinction in fresh water, presumably as a result of competition with the better equipped bony fish.

The dominant fresh-water predators thus arose from one of the lowly mud-grubbers that made their way into fresh water, but they became so highly adapted to predation that they spread to all the waters of the earth. This was not because they were predators in the sense of eating up everything in their way, but rather because there was no predator of their stamp before them, and by the time they came along there was plenty of ecologic room for such animals. There is evidence that some of the arthropods and mollusks have also gone back to sea, but they have done so on a much smaller scale, in all probability because they faced greater competition in the sea than did the vertebrates. Finally, as we shall see, the phyla that are dominant in fresh water include most of the organisms that made the even more difficult transition to land.

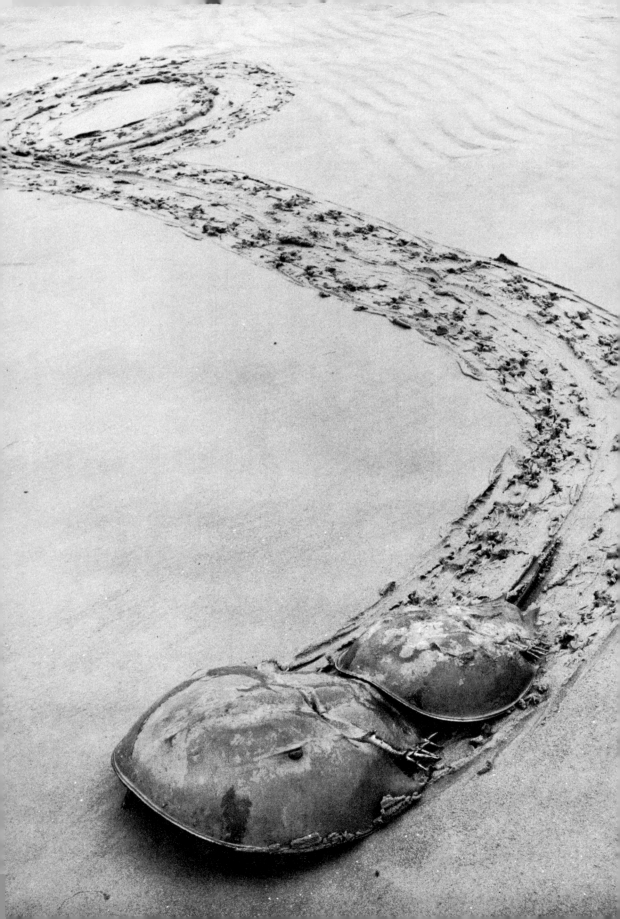

...AND ONTO
THE LAND

The most profound and obvious difference between the terrestrial environment and that of the seas, lakes, and rivers is the lack of water, and this lack produced an entirely different set of problems for those life forms that first moved onto the world's barren continental masses. On land there was no all-encompassing water to counter the pull of gravity, to prevent evaporation, to filter solar radiation, to modify temperature extremes, or to dilute the free oxygen of the atmosphere and so reduce its toxic effect.

But as different as aquatic and terrestrial environments are, an enormous range of conditions intermediate between them occurs where they meet—in the tidal zones and along river shores, shallow ponds, and marshes. It seems that the vast majority came by way of the river route, for the closest water-dwelling relatives we land creatures have and our most plausible fossil ancestors are fresh-water forms.

That fresh-water creatures were the ones to establish the first land colonies is not so surprising when we consider the features that had admitted them to fresh water. The impervious coat that protected them from excessive osmotic uptake of water served in some degree to protect their descendants against evaporation. Their rigid skeletal parts, which contributed to their capacity for moving against currents, served in their descendants as structural support. Because they had the means for directed locomotion, their descendants would be able to creep or trundle across dry land.

But prevention of evaporation demands a far more impervious coat than does control of

With a young male in tow, a female horseshoe crab plows across an Atlantic beach.

osmosis, and counteracting gravity on land entails modification of the skeletal architecture needed in the water. As a consequence, the so-called terrestrial members of all but two of the eight phyla represented on land are able to survive there primarily because of their small size and covert habits.

Familiar examples are slugs, land snails, and earthworms, animals that do not cope with terrestrial conditions so much as they avoid them. They are small enough to be covered by very little water, and they face no serious problem of support because strength and rigidity of materials is inversely proportionate to size. On land they are only active in water films, puddles, and extremely moist places, which are hardly more than extensions of the aquatic habitat. The majority of such forms can survive the occasional dryness of terrestrial conditions by encapsulating themselves or their eggs in a cocoon or an impermeable covering.

Small size may be regarded as preadaptive to terrestrial life, but even as it permits access to land it limits the degree to which the organism can take advantage of that environment. Encapsulation is almost certainly adaptive to life on land, but like small size it too limits the range of terrestrial conditions that can be utilized.

The only animal phyla that have succeeded in fully exploiting the terrestrial environment are the Arthropoda and the Chordata. The Arthropoda are represented on land by the mandibulate classes Insecta and Myriapoda (centipedes and millepedes) and the chelicerate class Arachnida (spiders and scorpions); the Chordata are represented by the vertebrate classes Amphibia, Reptilia, Aves, and Mammalia. The variety implied by this list of classes is emphasized by the somewhat overwhelming realization that there are eight hundred thousand species of insects alone, and by the fact that each of the vertebrate classes includes more species than the total of eighteen phyla of marine and fresh-water animals.

Between them, the arthropods and chordates have evolved terrestrial equivalents of every active mode of life developed in the sea. The only techniques they have failed to produce are those that are physically impossible under terrestrial conditions, such as the jet propulsion of cephalopod mollusks. Nor have they been content merely to fill most of the major niches on land; at intervals some of them, such as various insects (water beetles) and mammals (seals and whales), have gone back into water to compete successfully with forms that never left the water.

These animals achieved their extraordinary success because their rigid skeletal elements not only served as support, but eventually permitted them to become big enough to move about over great distances. In the arthropods, the exoskeleton also provided the needed protection against dehydration. In the vertebrates, coverings thick enough to do the same thing ultimately evolved. And so equipped, arthropods and vertebrates had a long lead on any potential competition. As a result they have had the field to themselves for about three hundred and fifty million years.

As in the transition from the sea to fresh wa-

That lungs had their start in a very low stage of vertebrate evolution is demonstrated by the fossil remains of Bothriolepis, *a small, abundant, bottom-dwelling fish that lived some 350 million years ago. Though equipped with jaws, head and shoulder armor, paired flippers, a flexible tail for swimming (not shown), and what scientists believe to be the beginnings of a lung,* Bothriolepis *disappeared leaving no descendants.*

ter, so in the transition from fresh water to land, plants had to lead the way. Many algae established themselves on land by living in extremely moist niches along the shores of rivers, ponds, and marshes. Because such places are little more than extensions of the aquatic environment, their occupation by animals such as protozoans, flatworms, and rotifers may also date from a very early time.

In time, certain plants evolved beyond the level of algae and gave rise to forms equipped to survive in all of the conditions of the land surface. These are the so-called higher green plants, which from their start are distinguished from algae on the basis of such terrestrial specializations as supportive tissues, impervious outer coverings, and surface openings for exchange of gases with the atmosphere. All of them, except the mosses and the liverworts, are also marked by internal conductive structures that transport water from roots to the upper reaches of the plant.

The earliest higher plants in the fossil record, the psilopsids, have water-conductive tissue, but like the mosses they are without roots and leaves. Higher plants, including the earliest ones, are classified into groups of increasingly complex structure as they acquired roots and leaves and as they developed a system of reproduction that was increasingly independent of surrounding water.

Two major divisions are recognized: those plants without specialized conductive tissues and those with such tissues. The latter includes, more or less in sequence of increasing complexity: ferns, horsetail rushes, and club mosses; seed ferns (an extinct group); cycads and conifers; and angiosperms or flowering plants—which means most deciduous trees and shrubs, herbaceous plants, grasses, and palms. With respect to independence of water in reproduction, the big break within the higher plants falls between the mosses, ferns, horsetails, and club mosses on the one hand, and the seed ferns, conifers, and flowering plants on the other. In the former group, fertilization requires external moisture. In the latter group, fertilization is replaced by pollination; the pollen can be carried by wind and requires no moisture outside of that of the reproductive parts of the plant.

The biggest gap in over-all structure, however, occurs between the primitive water-dwelling plants, which are algae, and the higher green plants. In this the evolution of plants contrasts sharply with that of animals. The only connecting link between the primitive aquatic plants and the higher green plants is by way of the green algae, in which the photosynthetic pigment, chlorophyll, and the compounds in which food is stored are the same as in the higher plants. But since none of the terrestrial adaptations of higher plants are foreshadowed in algae, we must conclude that they had all arisen during the transition to land. (Unlike the animals, plants owe very little to preadaptation in their conquest of the land.)

Plants are probably most abundantly preserved in the late Paleozoic era. But the record of the vertebrates is so much better understood and provides a far clearer view of the transi-

In the colonization of the land, plants led the way. Not until plants had established themselves could the plant-eaters and the eaters-of-plant-eaters follow. Plants gained their first foothold on land about 425 million years ago. In another 100 million years the continents were nourishing the lush Carboniferous coal forests. Lichen, such as shown at lower left, were pioneers among plants in that they could live on bare rock and served to break rock down into soil. The ferns (which here border a Vermont stream) are descendants of larger ancestors of the Carboniferous period, while the dragonfly below (newly emerged from its nymphal skin) is a holdover from Carboniferous ancestors that had wingspans of two feet. The dragonfly, like all insects, evolved as a terrestrial animal, and its success has been based on such insect features as small size and the capacity for flight.

tional stages that it affords a more useful clue to environmental conditions and so provides the more complete historic perspective.

As we have seen, the vertebrates made their way into fresh water as sluggish swimmers that fed by means of their gill system. Once in fresh water, they soon converted a part of that system into a new type of feeding apparatus (jaws) and improved on the respiratory function of the remainder; at the same time they perfected their swimming abilities by evolving paired fins. Still, none of these remarkable advances necessarily foreshadowed any future move to the land, for gills are of scant value on land and fins need a great deal of remodeling to be walked on.

Lungs, however, are another matter. Lungs are the respiratory organs of all land vertebrates and were probably present in most ancient fish long before any of them came ashore. A so-called blind pouch, a hollow, sacklike structure branching off the throat, in just the position of the lungs, is clearly identifiable in a well-preserved placoderm of Devonian age—one of the earlier jawed fishes. Lungfish, which were plentiful by the middle Devonian and are represented today by three survivors, have a true lung in that if forced to breathe only through their gills, they smother. Moreover, many kinds of living fish have a swim bladder, a gas-filled bag that helps control buoyancy and that is derived from the same embryonic sources as the lung. In some fish it is connected to the throat and aids in respiration. Thus the lungs, which have been auxiliary fish organs since the remote past, are decidedly

preadaptive to life that has moved out of water.

Yet another important preadaptive feature among the fishes was an ossified vertebral column, which was gradually evolved by the bony fish (Osteichthyes) that arose from placoderm stock in the middle Devonian period. This most essential development was closely related to the evolution of paired fins into legs and feet, and to understand both we must take a closer look at the Devonian bony fish, three kinds of which may be recognized. There is no telling how these differences arose, but as we shall see, they proved crucial to subsequent evolution.

In one group, the subclass Crossopterygii, the base of each paired fin projected from the ventral flank of the body as a muscular lobe, supported by a bony skeleton, while the fin proper was supported by a fringe of fairly short horny rays that sprang from the margin of the lobe. Crossopterygii means literally, fringe-fin, but as it is the lobe, and not the fringe, that is significant in evolution, we had best refer to these fish informally as "lobe-fins." The brain case of lobe-fins is hinged in the middle, which evidently permitted the front half of the skull to swing upward when the mouth was opened, thus increasing the gape of the jaws. Lobe-fins were moderately large (ranging from the size of brook trout to that of salmon). They were a predaceous fish with longish jaws well-armed with conical teeth, and thick, bluntly cylindrical bodies not particularly specialized for speed.

The second group, Dipnoi (lungfish), were much like the lobe-fins in shape and size, even

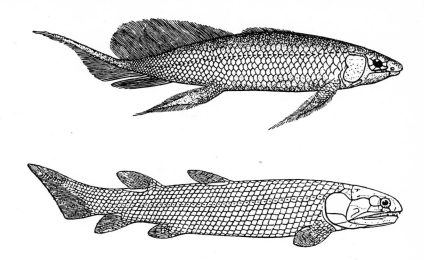

to the possession of lobed fins. Their skulls, however, are not comparable to those of any bony fish, and their jaws and large crushing teeth are more like those of certain sharklike animals. While the lobe-fins arose from one line of placoderms, it appears that the lungfish arose independently from another; if so, the general resemblance between lobe-fins and lungfish is due to parallel evolution.

In the third group of bony fish, the subclass Actinopterygii or ray-finned fish, the bony skeleton of the fin base is buried in the muscles of the body wall. The brain case lacks the joint found in lobe-fins, jaw gape being increased in predators by mobility of the upper jaw bones. The earliest ray-fins look rather like the earliest lobe-fins but are smaller and, of course, the fins are not lobed.

The ray-fins were rare in the Devonian period, which was dominated by lobe-fins and lungfish, but by the end of the period they began to supplant the other subclasses with a variety of forms ranging from slender, torpedo-shaped predators to deep-bodied, slow-moving, still-water fish. Some of the ray-fins entered the sea during the Jurassic period, about one hundred and fifty million years ago. Since then the group has radiated enormously, producing everything from minnows to marlins, and including such weird forms as flounders and ocean sunfish. The flounders spend their adult life lying on one side, and during their larval development one eye migrates around to lie next to its counterpart on the other side of the head, so that the fish comes to look as though it had been designed by Picasso. The

ocean sunfish is mostly a gigantic head and shoulders. In their adaptability, living ray-fins have not only invaded the deep sea, but a few types appear to be invading the land. The tiny mudskipper, *Periophthalmus*, an inhabitant of mangrove marshes along tropical seashores, actually spends most of its time on land, prowling the mud flats in search of small arthropods. On land *Periophthalmus* springs along by means of his enlarged front fins. When startled, he heads for water, but before plunging in he often skitters across the surface for several yards like a skipped stone.

The lobe-fins changed little throughout their history. Their big accomplishment, near the end of the Devonian, was to give rise to the land-dwelling vertebrates, collectively known as Tetrapoda ("four-footed ones"). Late Devonian lobe-fins correspond almost point for point with the tetrapods of the Mississippian period. They agree in brain-case structure and in pattern of teeth and superficial bones of the skull and differ primarily in loss of the bony gill cover and brain-case joint in the early tetrapods. The bones of the paired fins are comparable to the bones of the tetrapod leg and foot, and in certain advanced lobe-fins the spinal column consists of bone rather than cartilage, and the elements of the column correspond precisely to the backbone elements of the earliest tetrapods. *Ichthyostega*, from the early Mississippian or late Devonian, is officially a tetrapod because he has feet and lacks a bony gill cover, but he is so close to the lobe-fins that on his tail he still has a fish fin supported by horny rays.

The oldest known living vertebrate, a classic and fearsome-looking "living fossil," is shown in a rare photograph taken a few years ago 130 feet down in the Indian Ocean. A lobe-fin fish measuring about four feet long, Latimeria looks not unlike his ancestors of some 150 million years ago. It was fish such as this that first struggled onto land on their paddle-like fins and gave rise to frogs, crocodiles, and, eventually, to man.

The fresh-water deposits in which fossil lobe-fins are found were evidently laid down in the lower reaches of large rivers, the margins of which were marshy and dotted with ponds and oxbow lakes; their most ubiquitous feature is evidence of alternate flooding and slack water stages. Lungfish are also abundant in these beds, and since living lungfish have changed little since the Devonian, we may utilize their habits and environment to interpret those of the Paleozoic vertebrates.

The three kinds of living lungfish dwell in marshy pools that either become stagnant or dry up completely during prolonged drought. They can live in such a marginal environment because of their lungs, for when the water is too warm or too polluted with organic material, they simply breathe free air by rising to the surface. The few ray-fins associated with living lungfish include fish in which the swim bladder functions as a lung, or which, like the carp, can aerate the surrounding water by bubbling free air through their gills. The fish that live in these environments are characteristically sluggish, for they have no current to contend with, and they are relatively big fish in small ponds. An important mode of locomotion in living lungfish is their ability to walk about on the bottom of the pool on the tips of the fin lobes.

Some lungfish are able to survive complete drying when they are out of the pool in which they live by burrowing into the mud and secreting a cocoon of mucus around themselves. Their metabolism slows to a very low level, where it remains until they are freed of the cocoon by returning water. (Cocooned African lungfish are sometimes packed in tin cans for distribution—alive!—to biologic supply houses and aquariums all over the world.)

Thus the abundance of lungfish in late Paleozoic deposits corroborates evidence of periodic polluting or drought, and the associated fossil fauna bears this out. Lungfish and lobe-fins shared their environment with certain placoderms and a few ray-fins during the Devonian, and with ray-fins, fresh-water sharks, and a variety of tetrapods in the later Paleozoic. The presence of lunglike structures in the primitive placoderms suggests that lobe-fins and early ray-fins must also have had lungs, which are, of course, part of the basic equipment of the tetrapods. All of the vertebrates except the ray-finned fish appear to have been of sluggish habit, and the ray-fins were not fast-swimming types. The placoderms were bottom-dwellers, and lungfish, lobe-fins, and tetrapods alike probably spent much time ambulating about on the bottom.

It appears that lungfish hit upon their method of waiting out dry seasons in the late Paleozoic, for in deposits of Pennsylvanian and Permian age we find peculiar columnar structures of sediment that often contain lungfish teeth and bones. It seems reasonable to conclude that these are the former burrows of lungfish. Their habit of sleeping out the dry seasons served them well from the end of the Paleozoic to the present; but it never brought them into effective contact with the land.

Lobe-fins, on the other hand, evidently never went in for burrowing. Presumably their bony spinal column and stoutly lobed fins

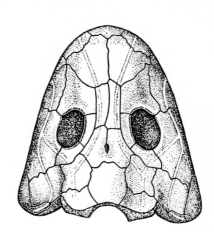
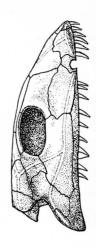

equipped them better for actually getting out of water, which became their specialized method for surviving drought. When the pool in which they were living shrank to no more than a mudhole, these fish capitalized on their ability to breathe air by leaving the water entirely. By means of a wriggling motion in which the paired fins served as pitons to get a grip in the mud, they made their way from pool to pool until they reached one of more satisfactory size or longevity. This locomotion at first must have been but little more effective than that of the proverbial fish out of water, and it was strictly an expedient measure. Its whole selective advantage lay in giving the animals another chance in another body of water. They probably did not feed while out of water, for the connection between the back of the skull and the shoulder, by way of the bony gill cover, obstructed the head movements necessary to grab prey on land.

But in their struggle from one pool to another, any modification that would make the trip easier would be strongly selected for. Smaller fish would have an initial advantage because support would be less of a problem than for larger fish. At the same time, a lower limit on size was probably imposed by the distances between pools. Land locomotion requires more pronounced flexing of more of the body than swimming does, and so there must have been selection for flexibility. Greater force is required to withstand gravity, which would select for longer and more heavily muscled fin lobes, while the rough terrain would select for greater maneuverability of the paired fins. But

as these modifications were speeding the passage from pool to pool, they were also making it possible for favored fish to cover greater distances or to spend more time on land. Lobefins, whose size was optimal for land travel, were small enough to have fed upon aquatic arthropods as well as smaller fishes, and since arthropods were well established on land by the end of the Devonian, there was a potential terrestrial food source available to them as soon as they were up to utilizing it. Selection for increased flexibility would have reduced the primitive connection between skull and shoulders, leaving the head supported only by the neck. Some animals would eventually become nimble enough to begin grabbing snacks en route between pools. At that point terrestrial selection would affect the feeding apparatus as well as the locomotor mechanism, and the vertebrates would at last have an economic basis for remaining on land.

So far we have discussed the tetrapods simply as the four-footed ones, because as yet we have dealt only with *Ichthyostega*, and his feet are the most convenient means of distinguishing him from his close relatives, the lobe-finned fish. *Ichthyostega* is the only four-footed animal on record for nearly thirty-five million years (or about ten times longer than man has been around), but beginning in the late Mississippian we encounter tetrapods in increasing numbers and variety. In general, the remains of these animals are less fishlike than *Ichthyostega*, and in life they must have looked more like big salamanders, or like lizards or crocodiles, with large, flattish heads and long, tapering tails. All had feet, but in most the legs were stocky, like those of living turtles, and in many they were proportionately very small.

The living tetrapods that represent this stage of evolution are placed in the classes Amphibia or Reptilia, which are distinguished primarily by their mode of reproduction. Living amphibians (frogs and salamanders) reproduce by means of a fishlike egg that has little yolk and no protective membrane or shell. The egg must be laid in water, and the young hatch as fishlike larvae, complete with gills, slimy skin, and lungs that function to control buoyancy rather than breathing. By the time the larva of most amphibians approaches reproductive maturity it has grown a set of legs, and when fully grown it loses its gills, the lungs begin to function in breathing, and the skin becomes less glandular and more resistant to drying. Most amphibians emerge from the water at this developmental stage, although some remain larvae all their lives and reproduce in that condition. Amphibians are thus functionally transitional, spending part of their lives as fish and part as tetrapods.

Living reptiles (lizards, crocodiles, turtles) reproduce by means of a large-yolked egg that is surrounded by the "amnion," a membrane developed by the embryo that retards evaporation and exchanges gases with the atmosphere. Reptiles do not go through a fishlike larval stage, but hatch as miniatures of their parents, complete with lungs and scaly skin.

In skeletal structure, Paleozoic tetrapods resemble each other more than they do living reptiles, and living reptiles more than living amphibians. While it would be reasonable to assume that the first tetrapods, being descendants of fish, hatched from a fishlike egg, we have no direct evidence that this was so, for there is a gap of some two hundred and fifty million years between these animals and the earliest record of modern amphibians. We must therefore sort out the Paleozoic tetrapods on the basis of other information.

In Mississippian and Pennsylvanian coal beds, for example, we find fossils of a variety of gilled aquatic larvae that correspond to certain contemporary adults in distinctive details of skull structure and are presumably immature stages of those adults. On the basis of the larvae we can assign the adults to the class Amphibia. In Pennsylvanian and Permian deposits we find tetrapod remains in which ossified gill bars are preserved, as though the animals had spent all their lives in water, like the living axolotl. These persistent larvae can also be called amphibians. Finally, we can tie most of these groups together by structural similarities, so that we may assign forms like *Ichthyostega* to the amphibians, even though we have no direct evidence of how they spent their larval childhood.

Reptiles have a much better fossil record than amphibians, and we know that they gave rise not only to present-day reptiles but also to birds and mammals. The record of mammals, modern reptiles, and dinosaurs can be traced step by step, in spite of numerous gaps, back to certain of the Paleozoic tetrapods, which can therefore be assigned to the class Reptilia. By sheerest luck we know that at least one tetrapod had reached a reptilian level of reproductive physiology by Permian time, for among the rare examples of fossil eggs is one specimen from the lower Permian of Texas. We may assume that the animal in question was one of those that we call reptiles, but just as we have no notion of who laid this rare egg, we are unable to say how many of our Paleozoic reptiles actually reproduced in the reptilian fashion.

The most successful of the ancient amphibians were members of the subclass Labyrinthodontia, a group characterized by large conical tusks of complex internal structure, located on the bones of the palate. The labyrinthodonts ranged from small insect eaters to large fish catchers; their heads were large and their skeletons were generally well ossified. Two lines, the temnospondyls and the anthracosaurs, are recognized on the basis of differences in details of skull pattern and spinal structure. The temnospondyls are most readily derived from creatures like *Ichthyostega*, while the anthracosaurs are of particular interest as including the ancestors of reptiles. Both groups are present in late Mississippian deposits and early produced a line of animals which, having evolved so far toward terrestrial life as to have legs instead of fins, gave up the whole business and went back to life in the water. These animals were generally quite large, with enormous palatal tusks, a long, slender body, greatly reduced limbs and feet, and a long tail like a crocodile's. They were swimming fish catchers and probably came into competition with larger lobe-fins. They were not too successful, however, for the anthracosaurian fish catchers died out early in the Permian, while the large lobe-fins hung on to the end of the period.

The aquatic temnospondyls survived by taking another tack, developing a group (or several groups) of very flat forms specialized for seizing their prey by lying in wait on the bottom. These animals became the largest amphibians on record, attaining a length of seven or eight feet. They had absurdly small limbs and must have been poor swimmers because their tails are short. The secret of their success was in their jaws, which were shaped like a bear trap. Apparently they lay quietly in the mud with their enormous mouths agape and when something (anything) swam within reach—snap! The bear-trap type of temnospondyl, the last of the Paleozoic amphibians, became extinct at the end of the Triassic.

Meanwhile the anthracosaurs and other temnospondyls were evolving into small animals (such as *Seymouria* and *Cacops*) that were highly adapted to terrestrial conditions. The relatively modest size of these creatures probably predisposed them to specialize toward life on land, for it minimized the problem of support. The head was held by a stout neck and must have been highly mobile. The spinal column was bony and elements were held together by a relatively sophisticated jointing system, which contributed to the strength of the column. The length of the column between its supports (the legs) was relatively short, another modification for support on land. The tail was also short, not obviously adapted for swimming. The limbs, though short, were very stout and heavily muscled, and the feet were large, in some cases al-

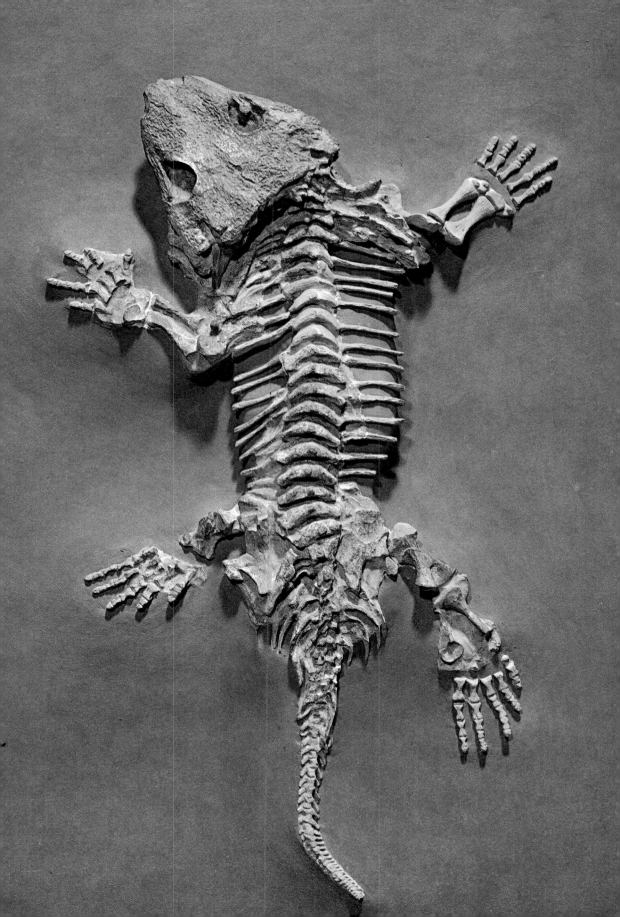

Among modern amphibians salamanders differ least from their ancestors in form and habit. But the most successful of modern amphibians are the frogs (the anurans) which are also among the most specialized of vertebrates: they have no tails and are equipped with very long, powerful hind legs. Frog history can be traced easily to the Jurassic, or 150 million years ago, while their ancestry seems to date from a time twice as far back.

most lizard-like. The hips were articulated to the spinal column by two specialized ribs, which provided the firm attachment needed for getting about on land; this feature is characteristic of reptiles generally but not of most amphibians. The skull was lightly constructed, and the teeth were proportionately small, as though insects were a staple of the diet.

It was from this part of the anthracosaur line that the first reptiles arose—in fact, the terrestrial adaptations just enumerated are essentially the distinguishing characteristics of the earliest reptiles. But the land-going temnospondyls were every bit as highly adapted to terrestrial life as the early reptiles and competed against them with modest success until well into the lower Permian. The factor that tipped the scales against the temnospondyls may well have been the invention of the reptilian type of egg, the oldest specimen of which coincides with the approximate time of their demise. We believe that temnospondyls never evolved such an egg, for many of them are persistently aquatic, and certain fossil larvae may pertain specifically to some of the land dwellers.

Adaptive similarities between terrestrial temnospondyls and anthracosaurs are another good example of parallel evolution, although some confusion does arise within the anthracosaurs, for they apparently made several stabs, during the Pennsylvanian, at producing a reptile. There are chronic arguments as to which, if any, of these animals is ancestral to the main line of reptiles. The terrestrial anthracosaur *Seymouria baylorensis*, of the Texas Permian period, combines amphibian and reptilian characteristics so neatly that, in between rows over its true nature, it serves as a prime example of an intermediate evolutionary stage. Currently it has been relegated to the status of an aberrant anthracosaur.

The invention of the amniotic egg by some derivative of the anthracosaur amphibians marked the end of the vertebrates' need to live in water. It was the consolidation of their bridgehead on the land, begun by lobe-finned fish and amphibians, and rooted in the prior evolution of the water-dwelling classes, that lumps them together as fishes.

The arthropods lack any fossil record comparable to that of the vertebrates, and so the stages in their emergence from water may be only surmised from the structure of living forms. One of the few things the record does tell us, however, is that by the early Devonian, about four hundred million years ago, arthropods were already represented on land by spiders, scorpions, and insects. The spiders and scorpions differ little from living forms, and the wingless insects belong to a modern group which is also characterized by winglessness.

The Devonian land arthropods are associated with the primitive land plants, psilopsids, many of which grew with their underground parts submerged in water and their stems projecting into the air. This confirms the reasonable guess that the arthropods, like the vertebrates, made their way out of the water via fresh-water swamps along river margins.

Aquatic ancestors of the spiders are poorly known from the fossil record, but there are water-dwelling scorpions from the upper Silurian

that can hardly be distinguished from their terrestrial descendants. Such evidence that we do have suggests that the chelicerate arthropods walked onto the land, just as their marine ancestors walked into fresh water. The arthropod exoskeleton and walking apparatus played its usual preadaptive role in this case, as did the small size of the original colonists.

Obviously there must have been a food source on land to attract them out of the water, and the association of land plants with the animals indicates that a flora was well started. But living chelicerates (spiders and scorpions) are exclusively predaceous. Barring the unlikely event that the first of them were plant eaters, they probably fed on small, soft-bodied animals that have not been preserved.

The earliest fossil record of insects shows that they were as small then as now, which probably accounts for their scarcity in the fossil record and suggests that small size was a preadaptive factor in their development of flight.

Embryonically, insect wings develop from flaps on the sides of the front body segments, which in the adults of flightless insects develop into rigid projections. It has been suggested that enlargement of such projections in unknown ancestors was an adaptation for gliding, a development feasible only in such small forms as insects. Mobility of the projections would confer additional advantage in terms of controlled flight, and changes in this direction would be favored. This is still an enormously "iffy" proposition, however, and we can say little more about it. All we really know is that in the hundred or so million years between the first flightless insects of the early Devonian and the giant dragonflies of the late Pennsylvanian, insects became pretty fancy fliers.

The advantages of flight, once attained, are obvious and account in part for there being seven hundred thousand species of insects, for these animals have the best of at least two possible worlds. Because they are small, insects have few problems of space, food supply (except when they overpopulate their environments), support, and shelter; but because they can fly they have the mobility of active animals many times their size. Because they are small and have a short life span, they can reproduce very rapidly; but because they are mobile, they can spread out quickly, to keep suitable environments well stocked with their kind, and to evolve to fit new environments.

In all animals many of the structures that had proved preadaptive to life in fresh water were also to prove useful on land. This is not as obvious in plants, and may not be true for them at all. But in both plants and animals, the structural adaptations that followed initial colonization of land were more pronounced than those which followed the colonization of fresh water, chiefly because of the lack of support and the dryness of land environments.

The distinctive features of the earliest land colonists are mostly responses to the demands imposed by these two extremes. However, much subsequent evolution, which produced the major terrestrial groups, consisted of structural and physiological responses to still another set of environmental extremes that we have not yet considered—temperature.

OF FAILURE
AND SUCCESS

Once on land, organisms had to contend with a formidable new environmental condition: because air absorbs and releases heat far more rapidly than water, the continental climate is characterized by sharp contrasts, both in time (night and day, winter and summer) and in space (from seashores to alpine meadows, from the tropics to the poles). Still, everything comes back to water, for the availability of water also varies in time and space, and extremes of temperature are compensated for by the biologic use of water. As a consequence, river margins provided the first creatures out of water with a proving ground to try out a variety of systems for getting along on land.

No organisms have ever become completely independent of water, and those which eventually established themselves in drier areas were able to do so only because they could utilize the relatively little available water or because they could conserve the water they carried with them. Plants were probably able to spread inland fairly soon after they had gained a foothold on land, for their root system preadapted them for drawing moisture from the soil, and insects must have followed after in short order, for many of them fed on plants while many others fed on the plant eaters. Insects were preadapted to dry conditions by the old reliable arthropod coat. In addition, sometime early in their history insects evolved a water-conserving method of excretion. Instead of flushing nitrogenous wastes from their bodies by the use of large amounts of water, as mammals do, insects extract water from the

swarm of sea birds known as sooty terns perform against a Pacific sky.

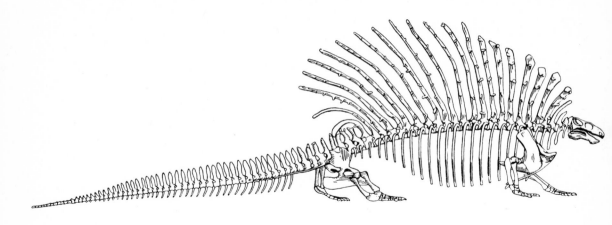

waste material in the intestine and deposit the waste as a solid particle. Because of their impervious coat and water-conserving physiology, insects can obtain the moisture they need from what they eat. And if this were not sufficient, the mobility of flight assures them of getting quickly and easily from one source of water to another. So small wonder that insects became the most numerous terrestrial group.

Reptiles of the Permian and early Triassic periods are abundant in the river and deltaic deposits. They often appear in assemblages of remarkable diversity, as though whole faunas were confined to river margins. But it was probably not until the end of the Triassic (which lasted fifty million years) that the reptiles entered the continental interiors, for, unlike plants and insects, they were in no way preadapted for dry conditions.

Like all animals except mammals and birds, reptiles absorb heat from the environment in order to function. Land-dwelling reptiles such as lizards, for example, maintain a constant body temperature by basking in the sun when they begin to cool off and by seeking shade when they get too hot. The higher the temperature, the faster the action, and many lizards function best with body heat that is considerably higher than ours. But the system has obvious disadvantages. At night, when their body temperature drops, lizards are unable to move very fast and become easy prey. To avoid being caught while torpid from cold or being killed by excessive heat, lizards seek shelter, and therefore spend an appreciable part of their lives almost totally inactive.

The dominant reptiles of the Permian belonged to the subclass Synapsida, also called mammal-like reptiles because their line can be traced from the end of the preceding period, the Pennsylvanian, to the origin of mammals in the late Triassic.

The earliest and most primitive mammal-like reptiles, of the order Pelycosauria, were the most active tetrapods of their time. They ranged from one to twelve feet in length and looked like lizards. The larger pelycosaurs, which were also the more common, had high, narrow heads, immense teeth, and were obviously predators of considerable consequence. In two distinct groups (*Dimetrodon*, a predator, and *Edaphosaurus*, a small-headed mollusk eater), their vertebral spines projected skyward like masts supporting a sail-like membrane that ran fore and aft. Quite likely, the membrane served to regulate heat. When the animals positioned themselves with the membrane perpendicular to the rays of the sun, heat would be absorbed rapidly and the animals would reach operating temperature much more quickly than animals not so equipped. When they turned themselves parallel to the sun's rays, the heat-radiating surface was greater than the heat-absorbing surface, and their bodies would cool down.

The more advanced mammal-like reptiles of the Permian and Triassic, members of the order Therapsida, had no such obvious apparatus for regulating heat. But their structure indicates evolution toward greater activity. Limb bones became longer, more slender, and were pulled in under the body, instead of being spraddled out, turtle-fashion. Trunk and tail were shortened, so that the therapsids no longer looked like lizards. Shortening of the trunk and tail reduced the tendency to move in the undulant fishlike manner; limb motion had become more important than back motion. There were changes in jaws and teeth that enabled more efficient mastication so that digestion proceeded more rapidly. Mammal-like air passages were evolved and a few advanced forms may even have developed hair. Even though such modifications would have enabled the therapsids to cope with temperature fluctuations better than their contemporaries, the animals apparently never strayed far from the river basins.

Another subclass of reptiles, the Anapsida, was also evolving during Pennsylvanian and Permian times. Unlike their contemporaries the pelycosaurs, the earliest anapsids were mostly small, lizard-like insect eaters. The anapsids gave rise to several lines, one evolving eventually into turtles, and another, the so-called Diapsida, giving rise to lizards, dinosaurs, and birds. Early diapsids were small and inconspicuous, slender of body, long of leg, big-footed, and, it appears, better adapted to getting about on dry, open ground than were any of their contemporaries.

Modern lizards and birds, derived from diapsid stock (their skull structure is comparable), are basically water conservers. Lizards and birds excrete nitrogenous material as nearly dry pellets or as slurry. They are not otherwise closely related, and as neither group is more restricted to an arid than to a humid climate, it is possible that lizards and birds inherited their water-conserving physiology from a common diapsid ancestor.

If primitive diapsids, then, had developed a water-conserving physiology sometime in the late Permian or early Triassic period, they would have been able to follow their insect prey into the drier interior. Their small size would have posed no problem in getting from one water supply to another, for with their water-conserving ability they could dispense with such treks, obtaining all the moisture they needed from their food.

Diapsids that lived close to watercourses had to remain small and inconspicuous to avoid competition with the then dominant therapsids. But those that entered the interior had no competition, for they were the first vertebrates to invade the area. So it could not have been long before they started preying on each other as well as on insects, and the more successful of them soon became relatively large, rapidly moving meat eaters.

Some of these animals turned out to be the ancestors of dinosaurs, which first appear in the fossil record in the late Triassic. The most primitive dinosaurs were lightly built reptiles about six feet long that habitually ran or walked on their long hind legs. Weight was carried on the second, third, and fourth toes of the elongated foot, which as a consequence was similar to the foot of a bird. These early dinosaurs were also birdlike in their two-legged posture and in having hollow limb bones and a short and rigidly articulated trunk skeleton.

By the late Triassic period the dinosaurs

were large enough to compete with the therapsids, and when we first find them in the fossil record they are reinvading the river margins, evolving into large, four-legged, swamp-dwelling plant eaters (sauropods), large meat eaters (carnosaurs) that preyed upon the plant eaters, and a third group of two-legged plant eaters of extremely birdlike structure (ornithischians). Competition with such an array was too much for the therapsids, which responded by becoming extinct—but not before giving rise to the first mammals. During the ensuing one hundred and thirty million years, while the dinosaurs dominated the terrestrial scene, the mammals survived by remaining small and inconspicuous, and by staying out of competition with the dinosaurs, just as the diapsids had survived the previous period by giving the therapsids a wide berth.

The most publicized features of the dinosaurs are their great size and the fact that they have long been extinct, and one frequently hears that large size was an "overspecialization" that led to extinction. But extinction is the usual fate of all groups except the most inclusive, and the dinosaurs forestalled it for nearly twice the time that has elapsed since they disappeared. We must therefore concede that they had a fairly respectable career and may look more carefully at the meaning of their most spectacular specialization.

It is hard to see how the dinosaurs could have been as active as their structure suggests without some sort of control over body temperature; and their very size may have been the result of selection for a heat-retentive mecha-nism. The rate of heat exchange between any object and its environment is directly proportionate to the ratio between surface and volume of the object. With an increase in size, volume increases half again as fast as surface since it is defined by three dimensions, whereas surface is defined by only two. Thus the surface-to-volume ratio of a big object is smaller than that of a small one and it therefore cools off and heats up more slowly. In addition, body heat is generated by muscular activity; with larger size the muscles, and consequently the source of heat, increases in proportion to volume. Once trends toward large size were started, they would of course be accelerated in plant eaters because of their protection against predators, and in predators because of their advantage in exploiting new food sources.

The chief drawback of large size as a heat-retentive device is the hazard of overheating. Mammals and birds pant when they get too hot, cooling by evaporation from the mouth and throat. In dinosaurs, over-all bulk was often too great for panting to be an effective cooling process. As a consequence, the largest dinosaurs went into fresh water for protection against overheating. There they also found abundant vegetation to feed on and shelter against attack.

The fact that most dinosaurs were plant eaters also certainly contributed to their over-all success, for it gave them access to virtually every niche commensurate with their size range (chicken to whale size) throughout the Jurassic and Cretaceous periods. And added to that, they were probably not as rigid in their adaptive requirements as is sometimes thought. They had, for example, originated and evolved among Triassic and Jurassic floras and were presumably adapted to them; but at the beginning of the Cretaceous, these plants (conifers and cycads) were largely replaced by a very different flora, as the flowering plants took over. One might expect this to have been an upsetting if not lethal turn of events for the plant-eating dinosaurs; but instead they only thrived on the change: there were more kinds of dinosaurs after the start of the Cretaceous than before.

It is sometimes assumed that a sudden major change in climate at the end of the Mesozoic era was the chief cause of the dinosaurs' demise. However, other episodes of climatic change during the Mesozoic do not appear to have bothered the dinosaurs excessively, and the suddenness of dinosaur extinction may be more apparent than real. Dinosaur fossils actually represent limited intervals of time, and there are very long stretches about which we have no information. The best known collecting areas are in the North Temperate Zone, the most poorly known are in the tropics. Correlation between them is difficult and unreliable. We do not know whether presumed tropical time equivalents were deposited within a few years of their northern counterparts or are separated by a million years. It is therefore conceivable that the dinosaurs hung on in the tropics for some time after they had died out in the north.

What really did them in is not known, but without strong supporting evidence we should not explain extinction by single or catastrophic causes, or by causes outside of the biologic world. Such evidence as we have suggests that the causes were ecologic, a combination of factors in which climatic change and the evolution of mammals were most important.

In favorable times the dinosaurs lived as far north as southwestern Canada in the New World and northern Japan in the Old World, and with them lived the little Mesozoic mammals. When such northerly areas became too cold or too seasonal, as they apparently did on occasion, the dinosaurs became extinct locally but survived in more equable areas to the south. When things improved, the dinosaurs moved north again.

The early Mesozoic mammals were more like therapsid reptiles than like the living mammals we know. But they undoubtedly had hair, and their more flexible temperature control system probably gave them greater tolerance over seasonal extremes than that of the dinosaurs. Each time the dinosaurs were forced out of the north, the mammals would stay on and would have the place to themselves for a while. So long as they were around, the dinosaurs exercised a strong selective effect on the emerging mammals, but the intervals gave the mammals an opportunity for a little experimentation. They were evolving, becoming more like modern mammals and perhaps getting a bit smarter, but never quite breaking out of their furtive habits because the dinosaurs kept coming back.

Ultimately the mammals perfected the temperature control system that had been begun

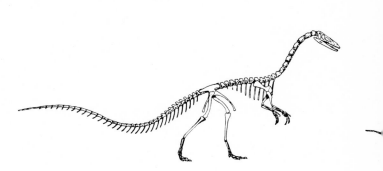

These skeletons belong to three small, highly agile, carnivorous dinosaurs that were equipped with grasping "hands." They are, from left to right: Coelophysis (from the Triassic), which was about eight feet long; Coelurus (from the late Jurassic), which was only about six feet long; and Ornithomimus (from the Cretaceous), which, being about eight feet long, was about the size of and much resembled a modern-day ostrich.

by the therapsids. They evolved the mammalian method of reproduction, in which the young are born alive and nourished with milk until able to fend for themselves. We do not know when or how these features were evolved, for they are not reflected in skeletal structure. But the skin glands that produce milk are believed to be modified sweat glands, so that this device must have followed the achievement of a mammalian level of temperature control.

Such a combination of features would have given the mammals an edge over the dinosaurs in terms of continuous activity and made them even better able to cope with seasonal changes. As a result, the mammals would probably increase and diversify each subsequent time the dinosaurs were driven out by climatic change. And ultimately this would alter the northerly environment in such a way that the big reptiles could not return when the climate improved. With climatic oscillations continuing over a long time, the returning dinosaurs would find larger and larger areas closed off to them until they were finally restricted to the tropics. And by then, or perhaps before, the more advanced mammals would have begun to penetrate tropical regions, and the days of the dinosaurs were numbered.

The main difficulty with an ecologic explanation of dinosaur extinction is that it does not account for other extinctions that took place in the sea at about the same time. Among the important marine animals that disappeared at the end of the Cretaceous are the ammonites, a group of shelled cephalopods; the mosasaurs, seagoing lizards up to twenty feet

in length; and the plesiosaurs, a reptilian group of uncertain origin and bizarre appearance. There are ecologic factors that may be common to the extinction of all of them, such as the radiation of modern types of sharks during the late Cretaceous, and undoubtedly there are other ecologic factors specific to each case. But the coincidence in the extinction of a large variety of organisms suggests a universal factor that can scarcely be guessed at.

The Mesozoic era, dubbed the Age of Reptiles, lasted about one hundred and seventy million years, and although dinosaurs dominated it, they were by no means the whole show. Along with the seagoing reptiles just mentioned, two other groups also flourished: the ichthyosaurs, which became extinct in the early Cretaceous, and the sea turtles, which we still have with us. The ichthyosaurs had the most sharklike appearance of all the marine reptiles and so probably went about their business in much the same fashion. Their early extinction may have resulted from immediate competition offered by sharks.

Then, too, in the middle of the Mesozoic (during the Jurassic period), certain reptiles developed a capacity for flight. Both the flying reptiles (pterosaurs) and our modern-day birds are derived from the same line of evolution that led to dinosaurs, but they managed flight in very different ways and are not closely related. The pterosaur wing was a leathery membrane supported on an enormously elongated fourth finger; the flight muscles were relatively weak; and the hind limbs were absurdly small. Pterosaurs were primarily gliders, and the poor

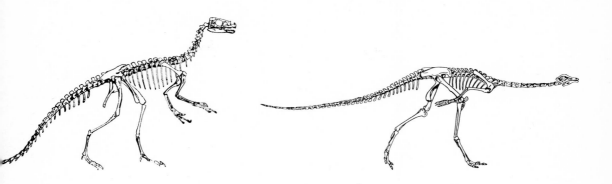

development of their hind limbs suggests that they originated from climbing animals. The bird's wing, by contrast, consists of feathers attached to the hand and forearm and has the potential for much finer control; flight muscles on birds are usually very powerful; and the hind legs are almost always well developed. Bird flight may well have begun by flapping, although the powerful hind limbs suggest that the ancient ancestral bird was a runner much like a dinosaur.

Unfortunately, the earliest fossil pterosaurs offer no hint as to the nature of their ancestral form. However, the earliest known bird, *Archaeopteryx* (ancient wing), is a beautiful example of a "missing link" that has been found. It looks like a tiny dinosaur—but with feathers. Unlike nearly all other birds, the beaklike jaws are armed with teeth; the fingers are separate; there is a long, slender tail; and the breastbone, hip, and trunk skeleton are no more specialized than those of a dinosaur. The birds mark a magnificent peak of specialization in the reptilian line. Moreover, they have, quite independently, evolved a temperature-control mechanism comparable to that of mammals in all respects. Poor as their fossil record is, it does show that they evolved rapidly during the Cretaceous period; and their abounding success probably sealed the fate of the pterosaurs.

It is still a matter of controversy whether the climatic change at the end of the Cretaceous was toward colder or warmer conditions. For we do not really know what the climatic tolerance of dinosaurs was; nor can we be certain that the climatic requirements of the organisms we use as indicators (crocodiles, turtles, various plants) were the same then as they are now.

The farther back in time we go, the less familiar the organisms with which we must deal, and thus the less reliable our conclusions about climate. For example, the wood of Permian and Triassic trees often shows annual rings that are thought to reflect seasonal changes from wet to dry conditions (since the flora gives the impression of a tropical climate). But because no living flora is closely comparable, there is the possibility that the changes were from warm to cold. Seasonal changes in temperature—rather than humidity—during the early Mesozoic have been suggested as the chief selective factor in the origin of mammalian and dinosaur temperature-control systems.

But it is in the next era, the Cenozoic, that the biologic evidence becomes more reliable. Here the record is more complete and the preserved organisms show progressively greater affinity with living forms. From the beginning of the era (some sixty-five million years ago) to the present, climatic zones become increasingly distinct, not only because of improvement of the record, but because of actual change. The Cenozoic records a trend from widespread warm, humid conditions following the end of the Cretaceous to generally dry, cold conditions like those of the present day throughout the world. The whole era is the cooling part of a very long cycle of climatic change that culminated in the most recent episode of continental glaciation beginning about a million years ago.

It was this trend, interrupted or reversed

from time to time, that provided most of the opportunities for the major plants and animals to evolve to their present form. Except for the marine mammals (whales, porpoises, seals, walruses), such opportunities did not lead away from the land, and as a result the changes they produced were not nearly as fundamental as most of those we have examined thus far. Even the extensive structural modifications of the marine mammals are superimposed upon what remains a basic mammalian pattern, and no new taxonomic groups above the rank of order have appeared during the past sixty-five million years.

Even before the end of the Mesozoic, the major groups had achieved their basic structure: birds and most insects in the Jurassic period or earlier; flowering plants, except the grasses, in the early Cretaceous; and mammals of modern form and the grasses at the tag end of the Cretaceous. These groups evolved through the Cenozoic as an interlocking ecologic complex, a study of which may be keyed to the best record, that of the mammals.

The evolution of mammals after the end of the Mesozoic, like that of ray-finned fish after the Paleozoic, is a matter of their devising different ways of making a living in a single broad environment. As a consequence, most of their diversity manifests itself in and is recognized by those tools of most immediate utility: teeth and feet. The significance of this overriding tendency impressed itself on early zoologists, as shown in the very names they bestowed upon the larger orders of mammals: Insectivora (insect eaters), Carnivora (meat eat-

Spectacular among herbivores was Stegosaurus stenops, *a ten-ton dinosaur that had a brain the size of a ping-pong ball and a larger spinal nerve center (sometimes erroneously called a second brain) to operate hind legs and tail. The big spinal plates, made of solid bone, probably served as protection against still larger, carnivorous dinosaurs. This reconstruction, built in 1911, is among the oldest in the Smithsonian collection.*

ers), Edentata (no teeth), Rodentia (gnawing teeth), Perissodactyla (odd toes), Artiodactyla (even toes). To be sure, a few names are not that descriptive, such as Hyracoidea (hyrax-like) and Lagomorpha (rabbit-shaped)— which are not much help if you are unfamiliar with a hyrax or a rabbit.

Insectivores, the earliest of the advanced mammalian line, were present in the Mesozoic, and since many of their features can be traced into more specialized animals, it is probable that they were close to the ancestral stock of Cenozoic mammals. Insectivores are still around in goodly numbers and very nicely illustrate the basic structure of such forms. Shrews, for example, the most generalized living insectivores, are small, seclusive, and savage (a few of these traits typify certain human females), as their Mesozoic ancestors almost certainly were also. Some of their characteristics, such as the five-toed, clawed foot, were inherited with hardly any change from their therapsid ancestors. Other obvious features, such as specialization of spinal column and teeth, though foreshadowed in therapsids, are strictly mammalian.

The spinal column of the trunk is subdivided into a rigidly articulated thoracic region that supports the ribs and a flexible lumbar region behind the thorax. In mammals, all motion of the trunk takes place in the lumbar region and is most powerful in an up-and-down direction, although it can also be moved from side to side in the old reptilian way. (The most graphic demonstration of these motions are the bumps and grinds, respectively, of that nearly extinct species, the burlesque queen.) This emphasis on up-and-down motion of the lumbar spinal column accounts for important mammalian specialties. Small mammals bound along by flexing and extending the lumbar column in a vertical plane, and whales swim in the same way, which explains why their flukes are horizontal instead of vertical, like the tail of a fish.

In the insectivores of the late Mesozoic era, the number of teeth became reduced to forty-four, which included incisors (for nipping or cutting), a canine (for stabbing), and molars (for shearing and crushing). The animals were (and still are) flat-footed, and their toes were well separated and had some grasping ability. Though primitive for a mammal, such feet are well suited for the insectivores' way of life: they are so small, any terrain is more or less rough underfoot, for which they need the flexibility of the five-digit foot; and speed over long distances is not important, since they are small enough to find cover in almost any nook of the forest floor.

Without deviating far from a basic pattern of skull and teeth, the insectivores produced such diversified forms as moles and hedgehogs. Even in the bats (which are placed in the separate order Chiroptera), the skull and teeth are essentially those of the insectivore; the specializations for flight have been superimposed upon an anatomical pattern not greatly different from that of a mole or shrew.

Although the diet of most living insectivores consists chiefly of insects, many are able to utilize a variety of plant materials, and while their success and longevity are no doubt due to

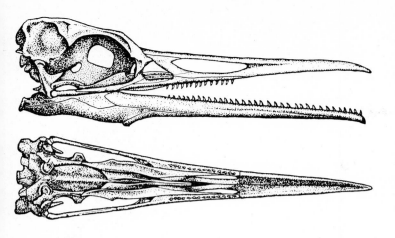

the abundance of insects, they gave rise to other orders of mammals because of their dietary adaptability.

From Insectivora to Primates is a short evolutionary jump, for there is simply no telling whether the living tree shrews are specialized arboreal insectivores or archaic primates. In addition, insectivore traits of teeth, anatomy, and diet remain prominent in those animals that zoologists agree are indeed archaic primates. The grasping hand with opposable thumb (and big toe) so characteristic of primates is essentially the adaptation of insectivore-like hand and foot to arboreal conditions, and primate dental characteristics have arisen as adaptation to the food most abundant in the trees—fruit, flowers, and leaves (as well as insects). There is no question but that the primates arose very early from a line of insectivores that had wandered up into the trees (which would have been no trick at all for a shrewlike animal) and that had found life good there. Bats and primates are both very early offshoots of the insectivore line, for they are recognizable early in the Cenozoic, in the record of the Paleocene epoch.

One more group of small mammals that made an early start by getting away from the ground are the rodents. Their basic specialization is toward the development of grinding molar teeth and chisel-shaped incisors (canines are dispensed with), presumably for use on tougher foods such as nuts and seeds. The incisors are kept sharp by being continually whetted against each other, which, however, wears them down. Mammalian teeth do not ordinari-

ly last long under such treatment, but in rodents the roots of the incisors remain open and the teeth continue to grow throughout the life of the animal. Thus equipped, the rodents were so successful that they soon spread into all manner of habitats and remain to this day a large and ubiquitous group—rats, mice, beaver, porcupine, and so forth.

One of the disadvantages of the insectivores' small size is the very high surface-to-volume ratio that it entails. Radiation of heat is a serious problem to the smaller shrews, which must spend most of their lives in a frantic search for food and consume several times their own weight in twenty-four hours. Once the pressure of the dinosaurs' presence was relieved, many of the insectivore line were bound to break out of such a life by becoming larger, as the primates and rodents did.

The really big living mammals, however, evolved from several lines of insectivores that continued to live on the ground. The trend toward larger size among mammals that began at the end of the Mesozoic was emphasized in these forms, perhaps as a result of the wider choice of food materials, and almost certainly by the old story of protection against and advantage for predation. Increase in size was attended by problems of support, and because larger animals found concealment more difficult, rapid locomotion over longer distances became more important. As plant eaters gained a capacity for prolonged speed, so, to a degree, did meat eaters. And all this required extensive overhauling of the primitive insectivore limbs and spinal column.

Among the oldest and oddest of American mammals is the shy opossum. About cat-sized when mature, largely nocturnal, and equipped with a prehensile tail, the opossum is North America's only marsupial and has remained virtually unchanged for the past 100 million years. The opossum is best known for its habit of feigning death ("playing possum") when cornered, a unique protective adaptation that scientists are still trying to understand.

The crouching, mouselike pose of small mammals generally is related to locomotion in a series of bounds. But bounding, while effective for short distances, is uneconomic, for it requires a burst of energy at each thrust of the legs and back, and a structure strongly adapted to a bounding gait precludes effective trotting or walking. But if the animal's legs are oriented in a more extended position, they can be swung back and forth like pendulums and the creature can trot. Trotting, like walking, consists of continually falling forward, and most of the energy is spent in moving the legs forward sequentially so that the animal avoids falling on its face. Considerable energy is spent in getting started, of course, but for the long haul at continuous speed, trotting is the most efficient mode of terrestrial locomotion.

Motion of the lumbar region is minimal during the trot. Animals that trot effectively do, of course, use lumbar motion for sprinting; predaceous mammals like the cat or otter do so in a series of true bounds, and hoofed mammals use the gallop. But these gaits are emergency measures, used in matters of lunch or no lunch, life or death, when the inefficient expenditure of energy is only momentary.

With size increase, then, the limbs assumed a more extended orientation, and the lumbar region became shorter and considerably less flexible. In the pendulum-like limb motion of the trot, speed is most economically increased by increasing the length of stride, which led to two further developments. The length of the lower limb bones, hands, and feet was increased, and animals tended to walk on their toes, which added the length of instep and palm to the pendulum of the leg. Weight came to be carried on the middle two or three toes, and as the first and fifth toes, losing their supportive role, were an additional hazard, they were selected against and tended to be reduced.

Mammals of approximately this level of development are characteristic of the Paleocene, when the largest were about the size of sheep. They could trot, but their lumbar spinal column was still long and flexible enough so that emergency locomotion was closer to bounding than galloping. Though many animals had gotten up on their toes, there was as yet little reduction of outer and inner digits.

Among living mammals, the locomotor apparatus of most carnivores has remained at about this level of development. An assortment of hooved mammals, however, have progressed much further—in shortening and increased rigidity of the lumbar spinal column, in elongation of the limbs, and in reduction of side toes. Their most characteristic locomotive feature is that they no longer stand on their toes, but only on the terminal bone of one (order Perissodactyla, including the horse, tapir, and rhinoceros) or two (order Artiodactyla, including the pig, cow, and camel) toes, which is reinforced by modification of a claw or nail to form the hoof. In living members of these groups the teeth have also specialized away from the shearing and crushing action of insectivore molars. While carnivore teeth in general are designed for shearing and slashing, the hooved mammals have tended to lose the canines and to modify the molars for grinding.

The size increase that produced the basic structural specializations of living mammals took place for the most part in a well-watered forest environment. But the emphasis of specializations on prolonged travel at constant speed preadapted these animals to penetration of more open environments. From the Eocene on, the herbivores especially seized the opportunity to move into prairie or savanna and, predictably, were closely followed by carnivores. Such country made for still more emphasis on speed, as is clearly shown in the horse evolution line. Legs became longer and lumbar region shorter. Side toes were lost and the weight came more and more to be carried on the second, third, and fourth digits. The horselike animals of the Eocene had low-crowned crushing teeth for browsing on relatively soft forest vegetation. As they moved into drier and more open areas with harsher vegetation, the teeth became more resistant to wear, but remained low-crowned.

Starting in the middle Oligocene, however, the grasses began to dominate the open country flora, becoming an important source of nutrition. But the supportive structure of grass consists in part of silica, and in dry climates most plants are covered by a thin film of silica dust. Silica is much harder than the enamel of mammal teeth, and consequently such teeth wear very rapidly on a steady diet of grass.

In the late Oligocene, horses began to cope with the problem by increasing the height of their tooth crowns and developing molar teeth that continued to grow during the individual's life. And taking advantage of the openness of grasslands, they eventually reduced their side toes still more. By the late Oligocene some horses were already functionally one-toed.

Cats are more highly adapted to a carnivorous diet than dogs, which probably originated from a more omnivorous group. Cats have retained the skeletal flexibility of their ancestors as part of their stalking-bounding method of attack, and as a consequence most cats cannot maintain speed for long distances. The definitive characteristics of dogs were established only as they ventured into open country in pursuit of hooved prey. For dogs show many parallels with early hooved forms in limb elongation, toe reduction, and compactness of foot, and their chief hunting technique is to run their prey down. Both cats and dogs occupy open country at the present time, but dogs dominate the latter part of the Cenozoic record, no doubt because of the spread of the prairie environment beginning at the end of the Oligocene.

Artiodactyls invaded open country along with the horse, reducing the side toes and evolving high-crowned, continually growing grinding teeth. By the Pliocene, they had surpassed the horses to dominate the open-country fauna, as they do today wherever they have not been wiped out by man. Their great advantage lay in the development of cud-chewing. Cud chewers spend part of their time cropping plant material in the open and storing the fodder in a special compartment of the stomach. Once the compartment is full they retire to cover, and, regurgitating the material

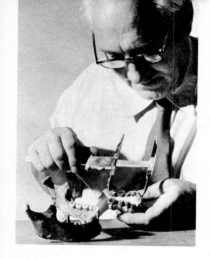

bit by bit, grind it up for proper digestion at their leisure. In this way they have to spend less of their time in an exposed position, vulnerable to attack. Cud-chewing may have suited the artiodactyls too well to a browsing habit along the margins of forests, for they lagged behind the perissodactyls in exploitation of the prairie. Their sudden rise to dominance in the Pliocene occurred when some of them acquired high-crowned grazing teeth.

The increasing numbers of running grazers in the fossil record does not mean that these animals replaced the browsers, for browsing perissodactyls (tapir and rhinoceros) and browsing artiodactyls (deer, hogs, and hippopotamus) maintained themselves and evolved in their own directions throughout the Cenozoic. What it does mean is that from the middle of the Cenozoic on, the drier environment of prairie became increasingly widespread, so that there was a lot more room for grazers.

But perissodactyls, artiodactyls, cats, and dogs were by no means the whole story of Cenozoic mammalian evolution. There were also the elephants. In obtaining large size, elephants had to dispense with all gaits except the walk, but they nevertheless maintained themselves in open country because even at a walk they could cover so much ground. Like the other hooved mammals, the elephants started with low-crowned browsing teeth, but true elephants and mammoths evolved high-crowned, continually growing teeth while the browsers or mastodons (an extinct group), continued to plod along almost down to the present with low-crowned teeth.

Then there were all manner of various small carnivores and about a dozen smaller orders that include such animals as the sloths, aardvarks, and anteaters of various persuasions. Among the more interesting are several extinct orders that evolved in isolation in South America. These animals paralleled all the specializations of perissodactyls and artiodactyls without being closely related to either, but they were wiped out by invading competition from the north when the rising Isthmus of Panama reconnected South America to the rest of the world in the late Miocene or early Pliocene.

The rise of the Panama land bridge was evidently a part of general continental uplift that led to the present very high stand of all continental areas. Uplift accompanied the cooling and drying trend of the Cenozoic that culminated in the continental glaciation of the Pleistocene epoch, and it may have been an important factor in its development. For the rise of land masses obstructs the global circulation of air and water and thereby exaggerates regional climatic differences. Dry climates become drier and cold climates become colder; mild climates of seacoasts and tropics are reduced in area.

Pleistocene glaciation was just such a regional phenomenon, for the ice sheet was more highly developed in the Northern Hemisphere than in the Southern (where it was restricted to mountains) and in the New World than in the Old. A simple cooling would not have produced the ice sheet, which required the accumulation of enormous quantities of water in the form of ice and snow. It is believed that the drying trends of more southerly latitudes were compensated in part by extremely heavy pre-cipitation over a long time in what is now northern Canada, and to a lesser extent in far northern Russia.

The Pleistocene lasted about two million years, but it was not a continual freeze-up the whole time. On the contrary, the four advances of continental glaciers were separated by inter-glacial periods when world conditions were generally milder than they are now, periods which lasted at least twice as long as the ten thousand years that have elapsed since the lat-est glacial retreat.

Although conditions where the ice lay were intolerable to most forms of life, the effects of glaciation were not catastrophic in any sense. The ice sheets were developed over a short pe-riod of time, geologically, but their progress was very slow in terms of the life of animal populations. Their effect, on a global scale, was to compress and jumble the earth's more northerly climatic zones. The most pronounced change of the glacial advance in tropical re-gions seems to have been on rainfall rather than on temperature. All through the Pleis-tocene, North America must have been teem-ing with mammalian life at the very foot of the ice front, at least during summer.

One characteristic of conditions close to the glacier was that the ground was permanently frozen to considerable depths, and plants grew on it only because the surface thawed during the summer. Under such conditions (which still exist in Alaska and over large parts of Siberia) the ground is treacherous, especially close to rivers, and animals coming to the water to drink are often mired and buried. This ac-counts for the enormous numbers of woolly mammoths found in the Siberian tundra and in Alaska, a few of which still have hair, hide, and bits of tendon preserved. The muck in which they "drowned" was very cold and acid (condi-tions that retarded bacterial decay) and ani-mals trapped near rivers at the end of summer might be frozen solid before decay progressed very far.

But no evidence shows the sudden death of large numbers at the same time, as is some-times claimed by theorists who still insist on a catastrophic interpretation of life history. On the contrary, mammoths have been found in winter and summer coats, with winter and summer forage in their intestines, and in every stage of preservation. Quite clearly, Siberian mammoth remains accumulated over thou-sands of years and under circumstances which are best explained in terms of normal biologic and geologic processes.

Much of the Pleistocene fauna of North America and Eurasia resembled that of the present: deer, bear, wolf, mountain lion, pec-cary (New World wild pig), bison, and prong-horn in the former; deer, bear, wolf, wild boar, auroch, and wisent (European bison) in the latter. But in America there were many ex-otics: saber-toothed cat, lion, elephant, horse, and camel. In Europe there was also a strong admixture of forms that now live (or lived) to the south and east: lion, leopard, jackal, hy-ena, elephant, rhinoceros, horse, camel, and an assortment of true antelope and wild sheep.

A few salient points may be noted about dif-

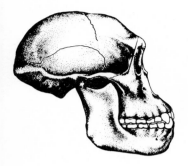 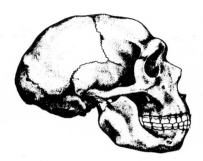 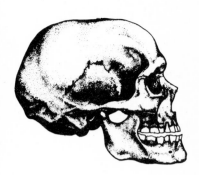

ferences between the immediate past and the present. The camel, horse, and saber-toothed cat are present in North America because that seems to be where they underwent most of their evolution; in other words, they were simply carrying on business as usual. The forms common to both areas are the result of dispersal across the then newly opened Bering land bridge: elephant, bison, lion, and hyena from west to east; horse and camel from east to west. The southerly elements of the Old World fauna indicate simply that they were more widespread then than now and became extinct in Europe while surviving elsewhere. And with the extinction of large Pleistocene mammals we come to a final phenomenon of the time, the origin of man.

For man is a child of the Pleistocene. Judging by what we can tell from the fragmentary early record, he originated, like his close relatives the great apes (gorilla, chimpanzee, orangutan, and gibbon), in forested areas of Africa or southern Asia, and most likely the former. Primates with apelike tooth structure and pattern are known from Miocene and Pliocene deposits, but the farther back we trace the scrappy record, the more the dental arrangements come to look human. Man's dentition is more nearly that of an omnivore, while that of the great apes is specialized for a herbivorous diet. From this it has been inferred that the common ancestor of man and the great apes was omnivorous, a perfectly respectable habit for primates, which are conservative offshoots of an insectivore stock. For that matter, even the chimpanzee, who feeds mostly upon vege-

table material, is known to prey upon small mammals when he feels like it.

At any rate, plausible common ancestors of apes and men lived in forests during the latter part of the Cenozoic era, in parts of Africa and Asia which are now savanna or desert. Anatomically they would be classed as anthropoid apes, but in behavior and social structure they are rather more like the baboon than the ape. With the drying trend of the time, open country expanded at the expense of tropical forest, and some of these resourceful primates tried their luck at life in open country, while others, no less resourceful but perhaps a bit more conservative, stayed with the retreating forests.

This was the point of departure between apes and men. The split was purely a matter of chance, the old story of one group following one opportunity and the other a different one. And there is no evidence that either group was in any way more aggressive or ingenious than the other. In brief, it was the choice that made the difference between apes and men, not the difference that made the choice.

The story of human evolution from this point is properly the domain of the anthropologist and has no place in a consideration that deals with few forms below the level of order. Fossil evidence from Africa indicates that man had attained human structure by the beginning of the Pleistocene and underwent much of his cultural evolution during that period. But the outstanding feature of this evolution is social organization, particularly with respect to hunting, for as soon as he left the forest, man had become a hunter. And it is this role that we may examine briefly, not for itself but for the environmental impact it had.

The larger Pleistocene mammals died out in Europe about twenty-five thousand years ago and in North America about ten thousand years ago. The European date corresponds to a high level of organization of the human hunting population, as indicated by the great prehistoric cave paintings of Europe. Man had understood the use of fire for thousands of years, and it has been suggested that about that time he began to use it for the organized mass slaughter of animals. But fire destroyed enormous areas of range as well. The larger mammals, never very numerous, would be especially hard-hit, and local populations would soon be reduced below the critical level. In North America the time of widespread extinction corresponds to the approximate time of man's arrival in the New World, and the same argument is put forth: that man killed off the larger mammals by fire drives.

Africa, however, looks like an exception, since man may have originated there, and in any case he has certainly hunted there at as high a level of organization as in Europe. And yet of all the continents, Africa supports the largest population of mammals comparable in size to those of the Pleistocene. But, the argument goes on, in Africa in the late Pleistocene there were even larger elephants and hooved mammals abroad in the land, all of which (amounting to 30 per cent of the population) are now extinct.

This view certainly makes good use of a number of interesting coincidences, and yet it has flaws. In Africa, for example, most of the large forms that died out in the Pleistocene were antelopes, and though big for their kind, they were hardly a patch on the surviving elephant, rhino, hippo, or giraffe. It is difficult to see how fire-driving would eliminate all of the big antelopes without taking some of these other forms with them.

Another difficulty with the theory is that many of the animals affected were prairie or savanna forms. Now fire-driving is particularly effective on a prairie because of the openness and dryness of the country. But the prairie habitat has evolved under the constant hazard of fires set by electric storms and is adapted by numerous features to quick recovery. So it does not seem reasonable that a few extra fires a year set by sparse human populations in an area the size of the Great Plains would make all that difference.

The horse in North America is a special case, for it became extinct coincidentally with the arrival of man from Asia, but repopulated the prairies quickly when reintroduced by the Spanish about four hundred years ago. There is no evidence of the physical environment having become momentarily unsuitable, and its extinction has been blamed upon aboriginal man. But another immigrant from Asia, the buffalo, had entered the New World shortly before man, and the appearance of a large variety of buffalo also coincides with the demise of the horse. Thus extinction of the horse in the New World can as well be ascribed to competition with the buffalo as to overhunting by man. The subsequent re-establishment in his-

toric times of the horse is then due, perhaps, to an alteration of the buffalo's ecologic position by the Plains Indians.

There is no question but that man is the most aggressive predator the world has ever known—and has been for most of the Pleistocene. But his predatory behavior must have evolved in an ecologic context, and for the greater part of his two-million-year history, man was probably little more abundant than any other large predator. The rise of man's numbers above a level suitable to a predator coincides with the beginning of settled agriculture, and most of the problems he now faces stem from two sources, both of them the result of this sudden change. One source is the constant Malthusian increase of numbers keeping pace with every technologic advance, and the other is the lag in the modification of man's behavior to fit his changed circumstances.

Perhaps the chief lesson evolution has for man is that, like all other organisms, he is subject to the ground rules of evolution, and his current predicament is evolutionary in origin. Man's original advantage stemmed from his tinkering, questing mind, which thus far has functioned like any other biologic attribute, under little control save that of the opportunism of organic evolution. The current result is overcrowding, destruction of the biological and physical environment, and on the social level, xenophobia. But man's mind is also capable of self-conscious appraisal of current conditions and of devising courses of action to fend off future evil. The question is, can these attributes, which are of very recent origin, mod-ify man's behavior soon enough to prevent him from poisoning himself or eating himself out of house and home?

Certainly immediate prospects are not encouraging, and yet the general outlook is not entirely grim. Every group of organisms that escaped from the old ancestral routine has started by coping with initially adverse conditions in its original environment, and has then proceeded to exploit these conditions. Coping with a problem is at the same time exploitation of an opportunity, and each successful step opens new opportunities. In the most successful organisms, the features that permitted the first steps are useful in subsequent situations. Man's brain permitted him first to cope with encroachment of open country on his ancestral forests, and then to exploit the open country. Now his problem is to cope with the results of his own cleverness, and we may hope that the factors that got him into this pickle will also serve to get him out.

It is sometimes suggested that control of our own evolution may provide a partial solution to our troubles, but this is true only if we know what we want to evolve into—which we don't. Before we worry about changing ourselves to fit a deteriorating environment, we should direct our efforts to conserving the present environment and to finding a sounder relationship to it. Much can be done along these lines, and much more has still to be learned. When we have established an objective environmental approach to our problems, we may start thinking about controlled evolution, and it may be that by then we will find it unnecessary.

A SMITHSONIAN PORTFOLIO

For the Europeans who first arrived on our shores, the North American wilderness was a place of unimaginable wonders and terror. But as the paintings on the next pages so handsomely illustrate, the flora and fauna were only a pale shadow of what they had been. The work of artist Jay Matternes, these paintings are details from the huge murals that line the hall of North American mammals at the Smithsonian's Museum of Natural History.

The scenes depict locations in Wyoming, South Dakota, Nebraska, Kansas, and Idaho, each representing a different epoch in the Cenozoic era. In all they cover some 60 million years of life in prehistoric America. The skin coloring and texture of the animals are largely hypothetical, since the fossil record leaves few hints of such details. The animals have also been grouped in far greater density than they would have been in life. But the over-all character of the backgrounds and the variety and anatomical structure of the animals are based on the most painstaking scientific research.

That creatures so bizarre and so beguiling as these two shovel-tusked mastodons once roamed the land we live on is a realization that brings the wondrous nature of evolution very close to home, and it explains in good part why the murals are among the most popular of all the Smithsonian exhibitions.

THE EOCENE EPOCH *began 60 million years ago and lasted 20 million years, during which time mammal life in North America flourished and most modern orders became clearly defined. The ancestors of modern carnivores appeared, along with rabbits, squirrel-like rodents, and the earliest whales. The biggest of the land forms was a rhinoceros-like creature,* Uintatherium, *which had huge, saber-like tusks and three pairs of horns.*

This scene depicts the area near the Green River in Wyoming during the second half of the Eocene, when the climate was a good deal warmer and damper than it is today. The lush vegetation included ferns, water lilies, palms, sweet gum, and sycamores. All the animals shown here are small— fox-sized or less. The three spotted animals beside the hollow log are early horses of the genus Orohippus. *The lizard in the clutches of two carnivores is* Saniwa; *the black, doglike carnivore is* Sinopa *and the fanged cat is* Machaeroides, *both of which became extinct too early to take a direct part in the dog or cat lineage. The three small animals at left are, from top to bottom,* Homacodon, Helohyus, *and* Metacheiromys. *The first two are from the most primitive group of artiodactyls (some of which gave rise to later-day pigs, camels, and cattle).* Metacheiromys *is a primitive armadillo. The two turtles at right look not much different than their present-day descendants.*

The tapir-like browsers at top are Helaletes; *the face peeking in at their right is that of a hyena-like animal,* Mesonyx; *and the clawed feet at upper left belong to* Stylinodon, *an offshoot of the insectivore stock that was dying out.*

117

DURING THE OLIGOCENE, *36 million years ago, along with numerous smaller forms, several huge mammals evolved. The savage pair below are* Archaeotherium, *which like other giant pigs flourished in the mild climate and savanna-like environment of the time. But the biggest mammals ever to live in North America were the* Brontotherium *(a full-grown member is shown opposite). Built like rhinos, they were hoofed herbivores armed with blunt, battering-ram horns. Some weighed as much as five tons and were eight feet high at the shoulder. The horselike animal in the foreground is an ancient tapir; the other, to the left, is a small rhino. The setting for both scenes is South Dakota.*

THE MIOCENE (OVERLEAF) *saw the expansion of grasslands and the spread of grazing animals such as those in this view of northwestern Nebraska about 25 million years ago. The dun-colored horses are of the genus* Parahippus, *and, unlike the older, smaller, forest-dwelling horses, they had teeth suited for a grass diet. The horned animal at far right,* Synthetoceras, *is related to the living pronghorn. Just above, making a fast exit right, is* Dinohyus, *a giant pig. To the left, rhinos of the genus* Diceratherium *rest in the shade behind primitive camels,* Stenomylus. *At far left is an amphibious, piglike* Promerycochoerus, *and a ferocious bear-dog,* Daphoenodon.

IN EARLY MIOCENE DEPOSITS *in North America the fossils of piglike, four-toed oreodonts (sometimes called "ruminating swine") outnumber those of all other mammals combined. Among the more advanced oreodonts was* Merychyus, *which combined features found in sheep as well as pigs. Though their bones are abundant in both Oligocene and Miocene beds, nothing like them lives on today. As in the preceding scene, these animals are viewed in Nebraska some 25 million years ago. At lower left is* Palaeocastor, *a burrowing, beaver-like rodent that lived much like a modern prairie dog. Of all living mammals, rodents are the most successful, with numerous genera and species thriving in every kind of habitat.*

THE PLIOCENE *began 12 to 14 million years ago and was characterized in North America by an increasingly arid climate. On the great open grasslands, numerous varieties of animals continued to flourish. At left, in northwestern Kansas, in a landscape that looks much like it does today, aquatic rhinos of the time* (Teleoceras) *and five lumbering, shovel-tusked mastodons* (Amebelodon) *retreat from a river, their customary habitat, as a prairie storm builds in the distance. The river, already at high-water mark, will soon be on the rampage as flash floods rush from the barren hills. Distantly related to living elephants, the* Amebelodon *were browsers with lower jaws more than nine feet in length.*

THE PLEISTOCENE (OVERLEAF), *which ended about 10,000 years ago, was dominated by the advance and retreat of great ice sheets that created climatic and environmental conditions of striking variety. North America was abounding with animal life, very modern in form, as this scene from Idaho, along the shallows of the Snake River, gives evidence. Shown here are wild pig and giant beaver, saber-toothed cat, ground sloth, water bird, reptile, deer, zebra-like horse, bear, and mastodon, many of which are now extinct. What exactly caused the "great dying" of the late Pleistocene epoch is still a puzzle, but one scientific theory suggests that the demise of the big animals at least may be linked to the arrival in North America of that most successful of predators: man.*

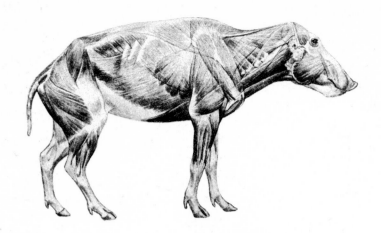

ARTIST JAY MATTERNES *is considered by Smithsonian paleontologists to be the foremost scientific muralist at work today. Born in 1933, Matternes studied at the Carnegie Institute of Technology, in the College of Fine Arts, and was later on the staff of the Cleveland Museum of Natural Science. Since receiving his first Smithsonian commission in 1956, he has completed nine murals and background paintings, each of which has required months of study and research, very often in the field. The musculature of every animal in his murals is based on numerous sketches (a sample is shown above) worked up from the latest scientific findings, or in some cases from clay models that he builds with the help of experts on the Smithsonian staff. Below, he is shown finishing the preliminary charcoal drawing of two peccaries for a new mural on the Pleistocene. (The view on the two preceding pages is from his preliminary easel painting. The completed mural will measure 12 by 19 feet.)*

APPENDIX

TIMETABLE OF EVOLUTION

3 BILLION YEARS

600 MILLION YEARS

500 MILLION YEARS

PRECAMBRIAN

PRECAMBRIAN

Estimates based on the oldest
known fossils place the origin
of life at about three billion
years ago. Though very rare,
such fossils (all marine forms)
include algae-like and fungi-like
plants, a few primitive shelled
animals, and imprints of soft-
bodied animals such as jellyfish
and worm burrows. The
scarcity of the record indicates
that most forms had not yet
developed hard parts (skeletons
or shells) capable of preservation. Nonetheless, all forms were
the product of previous
evolutionary processes of which
there remains not a trace.

BACTERIA

CAMBRIAN

This period marks the beginning
of an extensive fossil record.
Invertebrate animals of countless
varieties filled the seas as the
dominant life form, giving this
vast slice of time and the one to
follow the popular name, the Age
of Invertebrates. Trilobites and
brachiopods were the most
abundant invertebrates and
together comprise 80 to 90 per
cent of the Cambrian fossil record.
Trilobites were named for
their primitive three-lobed body,
which was covered by a chitinous
shell. A cross between a lobster
and a sea slug in appearance,
they averaged two inches in length,
though some grew as long as two
feet. Brachiopods were small
marine animals with a double-
valved phosphatic shell. When
their shell was opened, they
extended two coiled appendages,
known as brachia, to entrap food
particles. Sponges, early mollusks,
and worms were also present.
In fact, fossils from the
famous Burgess Shale in Alberta,
Canada, strikingly reveal the
great diversity of life at
this time. Little is known
about the plant life except that it
was limited to the sea.

ORDOVICIAN

Invertebrate marine life
multiplied, diversified, and
continued to dominate the
living world. The first corals
appeared and numerous mollusk
were present, including the
cephalopods. The forerunners of
the present-day squid, some of
these cephalopods looked like
snails. Others had shells
15 feet long, making them the
giants of the Ordovician seas.
Starfish and sea urchins also
inhabited the sea floor. Marine
plant life was made up almost
entirely of algae and seaweed.
The era's most important event
was the appearance of the
first vertebrate, a primitive,
jawless fish, an ostracoderm.

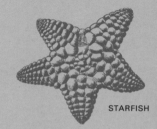

STARFISH

The jawless fish marked
the entrance of the Chordata,
a phylum which would
eventually dominate whatever
sphere it entered.

PALEOZOIC

SILURIAN

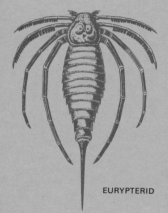

EURYPTERID

...ea life was very similar to that f the Ordovician period. Corals ecame greatly diversified and ome of the colonial corals were so rofuse that they formed huge eefs. Prominent among Silurian ssils are the eurypterids, orpion-like creatures who amed the sea floor. Though now ctinct, these animals were stantly related to the trilobites. he first primitive land plants arked another important dvance of this age, but their ssil remains are very rare. And llowing the plants came the rliest known land animals, milar to present-day scorpions d related to the eurypterids.

DEVONIAN

Many evolutionary advances occurred during what is also called the Age of Fishes. For the first time vertebrate life occupied a prominent position in the living world and bizarre and wonderfully advanced forms of fish developed. Fish by now had evolved to the extent that two major groups are distinguishable: the cartilaginous (sharks) and the bony fish (forerunners of most modern species). The active locomotion, jaws, and primitive teeth developed by the bony fish made them vigorous and aggressive predators; they were a marked advance over the jawless ostracoderm, who was limited to mud-grubbing along the sea floor. Some fish developed

BONY FISH

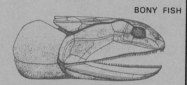

internal air bladders and muscular lobes on their fins: they, in turn, would become the first amphibians. Plants also made important advances as giant ferns appeared on the landscape.

CARBONIFEROUS

PENNSYLVANIAN

Marine life abounded as warm seas invaded the continent. Cup-shaped animals with feathery arms known as crinoids (sea lilies) were numerous and their fossil remains contributed greatly to the vast limestone formations of the period. Sharks were very abundant, with about 300 species churning the seas. Winged insects appeared. Plants thrived, especially on the edges of pools, shallow lakes, and swamps.

MISSISSIPPIAN

During this Age of Coal, giant-sized scale trees, scouring rushes 30 feet high, and true ferns flourished in swampy lowlands between recurrent invasions of the sea. Insects were present in copious numbers and varieties. Scorpions, spiders, dragonfly ancestors with 29-inch wingspreads, and 4-inch cockroaches all swarmed through the forests. Primitive reptiles evolved from the ranks of the amphibians to become the first vertebrates able to live full time on land.

131

PALEOZOIC

PERMIAN

MESOZOIC

JURASSIC

TRIASSIC

Widespread climatic changes led to the extinction of many plants and animals. A generally drying and cooler climate caused many tropical, coal-forming plants of the previous period to die out. Vertebrates made rapid and significant advances: in the seas fishes increased in variety and numbers while amphibians flourished in and near the rivers. Reptiles dominated the land and

EARLY AMPHIBIAN

reached an extreme degree of specialization. One group of reptiles, the pelycosaurs, which include the outlandish sail-backs Dimetrodon *and* Edaphosaurus, *are remote ancestors of present-day mammals.*

Reptiles achieved great diversity, lending their name to the entire era, the Age of Reptiles. Some of them became fully marine; two of the best known were the ichthyosaurs, which came to resemble sharks, and the plesiosaurs, which have been described as a snake threaded through a turtle. The most common of all Triassic reptiles was the phytosaur, a semiaquatic animal resembling a crocodile. By the end of the Triassic, early crocodiles began replacing the phytosaurs and small dinosaurs appeared. Though subordinate to the vertebrates, the invertebrate world also continued to expand. The seas were filled with reef corals, mollusks, and crinoids.
Of the flora, cycads resembling modern palms were numerous and conifers (cone-bearing trees) were very abundant. In fact, trunks of some of these ancient conifers are now preserved and form the Petrified Forest.
But the most significant event was the appearance of the first warm-blooded mammals, which ranged from rat size to the size of a small dog.

In various shapes and sizes, reptiles inhabited the land, sea, and air. While ichthyosaurs and plesiosaurs expanded in the sea, flying reptiles, called pterosaurs, glided through the air. Dinosaur

EARLIEST KNOWN BIRD

reached their peak and dominate the land. Both carnivorous and herbivorous, they grew to be the largest land animals the world has ever known. Some of the plant eaters were 85 feet long and weighed as much as 40 tons. Still another turning point was marked by the appearance of the first primitive birds, which were comparable to a raven in size.

CENOZOIC

CRETACEOUS

Among the highly significant events of the period was the appearance of the first flowering plants, including modern trees. Among the developing vertebrates, reptiles continued to dominate, increasing in abundance and variety. Dinosaurs became highly specialized. Most famous was Tyrannosaurus rex, a bipedal, flesh-eating monster over 40 feet long and standing about 20 feet high. But by the close of the period, for reasons still unknown, the dinosaurs were all extinct. One flying reptile attained a 26-foot wingspread. Birds became increasingly specialized—some forms lost their power of flight, becoming suited to swimming and diving, while others had well-developed wings and behaved like modern sea gulls. Mammals were still small, primitive, and inconspicuous.

TYRANNOSAURUS REX

TERTIARY

The Cenozoic opened with mammals replacing reptiles as the dominant form of animal life. From the simple shrewlike types of the Cretaceous sprang the forerunners of several of our

MAPLE LEAF

modern animals: horses, rhinoceros, elephants, zebras, and rodents—all of which appeared early in the period. Eohippus, so-called "dawn horse," stood 12 inches high; and the earliest elephants were trunkless and tuskless. Many mammals evolved only to become extinct soon after. Among them were the uintatheres, clumsy, small-brained, and elephant-sized, which had horns on their snouts and foreheads possibly for protection against their predators. Amphibians and reptiles decreased. Birds were modern in appearance. The flora was strikingly similar to today and hardwood forests and grasslands spread over the landscape.

QUATERNARY

Vast climatic fluctuations and the advance of the ice sheets marked the opening of the period and greatly affected the living world. Most tertiary animals became extinct while cold-adapted forms, such as the woolly mammoth, evolved. The advancing and retreating ice front caused vast migrations of plants and animals and altered their distribution over the world. With the end of the ice age, many animals such as the saber-toothed tiger, mastodon, and giant beaver became extinct for reasons still undetermined.

SABER-TOOTHED TIGER

Near the end of the Pleistocene, a new primate, Australopithecus, the earliest known species of modern man, made his appearance.

133

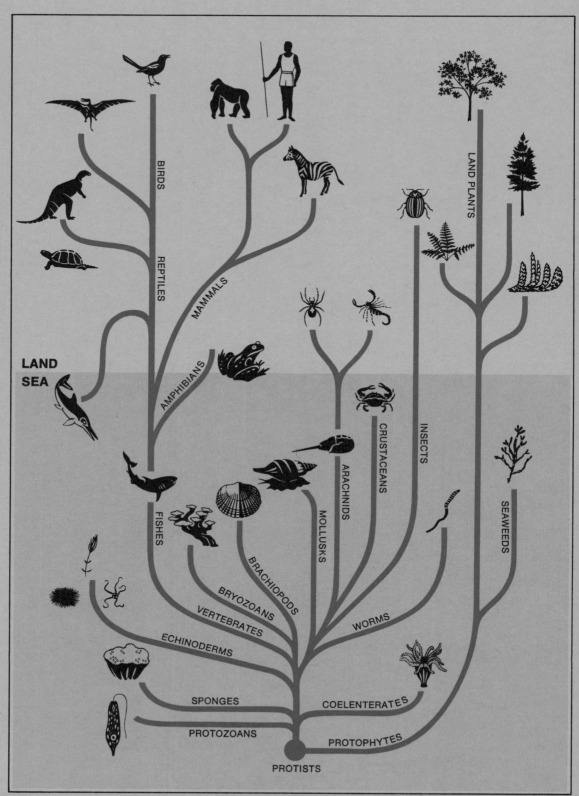

LAND
SEA

BIRDS

REPTILES

MAMMALS

AMPHIBIANS

LAND PLANTS

INSECTS

FISHES

ARACHNIDS

CRUSTACEANS

SEAWEEDS

MOLLUSKS

BRACHIOPODS

BRYOZOANS

VERTEBRATES

WORMS

ECHINODERMS

SPONGES

COELENTERATES

PROTOZOANS

PROTOPHYTES

PROTISTS

A SIMPLIFIED FAMILY TREE OF LIFE

THEORISTS AND EVOLUTION

American people. He warned that the evolutionists "are chasing a phantom in their search after some material gradation among created beings." In later years, however, Agassiz' dogmatic position (all species are distinct and separately created) softened. A year before his death he even admitted that Darwin's theories might have some validity if enough evidence could be obtained from all parts of the world to show definite genetic relationships between species.

AGASSIZ, Jean Louis Rodolphe (1807–1873)
Swiss-born American naturalist

"The resources of the Deity," wrote Agassiz, "cannot be so meager, that in order to create a human being endowed with reason, he must change a monkey into a man." The most prominent American naturalist to attack the views of Darwin, Agassiz was an atheist while young but grew increasingly religious with age. After receiving a medical degree from the University of Munich in 1830, he came under the influence of Alexander Humboldt, Europe's leading scientist, who helped finance him through a study on fish, which Agassiz laboriously classified according to scale variances. For the next decade Agassiz delved into glacial theory, upon which his fame chiefly rests. He was the first to point out the existence of a former ice age and the importance of the advancing and retreating ice sheets in altering the earth's surface. In 1846, due mainly to his work on fossil fish, Agassiz was invited to lecture in Boston; he then became a member of the Harvard faculty, on which he served most of his remaining years. During the Civil War he initiated a series of lectures to expose the dangers of Darwinism to the

BUFFON, Comte Georges Louis Leclerc de (1707–1788)
French naturalist

Born to wealth, Buffon had ample opportunity to develop his diverse scientific interests. After studying law and medicine, he found his niche as keeper of the Jardin du Roi, the French botanical gardens. His love of natural history culminated in the publication, over a 50-year span, of a 44-volume compendium called Histoire Naturelle. Throughout this popular work Buffon can be seen groping for an evolutionary interpretation of life, nearly a century before Darwin. He felt that the direct action of the environment brought about structural modifications in plants and animals that were transmitted to their offspring. He also noted that many animals had useless parts that slowly disappeared. From this he deduced that if parts

may disappear, why not entire species as well? Buffon was the first European Christian to state openly that the world may be much older than the 6,000-year limit imposed by Genesis. Despite such apparent daring, Buffon was known to alter his views when confronted with powerful opposition. He was elected to the French Academy in 1753.

CUVIER, Baron Georges (1769–1832)
French anatomist

Considered the founder of comparative anatomy, Cuvier was a well-read zoologist by the time he entered his teens. As a young man, he studied for government service, but financial problems forced him in 1795 to accept a position at the Museum of Natural History in Paris. It was here that he developed an interest in anatomy that led him to extend and correct Linnaeus' system for classifying species. The first to include the classification of fossils, Cuvier was struck by the fact that each fossil he found

was unlike the structure of any living species, yet closely enough related to be grouped in one of the four phyla he had established. Still, Cuvier could not accept the discovery as proof for evolution. He was, in fact, a militant antievolutionist who argued that fossil gradations were the result of periodic

135

inundations, after which new forms of life appeared. Fossils were therefore always remnants of periods preceding the most recent catastrophe. This explanation allowed Cuvier the comfort of being able to accept the Bible literally. A tough and able administrator who had never completely abandoned his political interests, Cuvier received several government appointments, including one as minister of the interior under King Louis Philippe.

DARWIN, Charles (1809-1882)
English naturalist

Born to a family that, for several generations, had been noted for its intellectual accomplishments, Darwin showed no signs of special talent in his youth. After flirting with careers in medicine and the church, he turned to the study of natural science. In 1831 Darwin left his Cambridge studies to serve as naturalist on what turned out to be the most significant biologic expedition in history. Along the coasts of South America, on the Galápagos Islands, at Tahiti, and in Australia and New Zealand, he took careful note of the plants and animals, their similarities and differences. From the sheer variety of species and the way they distributed themselves geographically, Darwin began to doubt the prevailing theory that all species had been separately created. For another two decades he struggled to find a better answer, and in 1859 he presented his conclusions in the world-shaking Origin of Species. All species, Darwin insisted, had a common ancestry, and the fate of any one species was determined by its ability to adapt to its environment

through a process he called natural selection. The book started a controversy that still persists. Both religious and scientific leaders quickly adopted fighting stances, while the gentle-natured Darwin resumed his studies. In 1871 he published The Descent of Man, which argued that man had evolved from subhuman forms. Loudly compared to Satan himself, Darwin endured it all with good humor, and by the time of his death he had won most scientists over to his view.

DE VRIES, Hugo (1848–1935)
Dutch botanist

Had De Vries possessed a lesser degree of integrity he might today be credited with having discovered the laws of heredity. But De Vries gave the credit to Gregor Mendel, whose brilliant experiments on plant genetics had preceded his own work by several decades. Mendel's work had gone unnoticed by the scientific community; De Vries discovered his monograph in 1900, on the eve of publishing his own results, which he thereupon presented only as confirmation of Mendel's work. (Two other

scientists, working independently, also came upon Mendel's paper at about the same time, and both also acknowledged Mendel's priority.) De Vries' work actually transcended that of

Mendel; in 1886 he had discovered that plant species produced new characteristics, called mutations, which were perpetuated in succeeding generations—a fact then known to animal breeders but missed by scientists. De Vries postulated that changes in species would tend to occur in sudden jumps, and his theory of mutations buttressed the arguments for the Darwinian view of evolution. His theory also challenged August Weismann's doctrine of the immutability of germ plasm, though it took later research to prove the correctness of De Vries' views.

HAECKEL, Ernst (1834–1919)
German naturalist

What Thomas Huxley, the great proponent of evolutionary theory, did for Darwinism in England, Haeckel did for it in Germany. In 1866, when he was professor of comparative anatomy at the University of Jena, Haeckel met Darwin for the first time. In his words, "It was as if some exalted sage of Hellenic antiquity . . . stood in the flesh before me." Haeckel campaigned for Darwin's ideas with such fervor that the Pope, following one of Haeckel's lectures in Rome, ordered a "divine fumigation" of the entire city. Haeckel's zeal carried him to speculations on evolutionary relationships among various creatures that were quite wrong and an embarrassment to Darwin.

His argument that all creatures in their embryonic development repeat their evolutionary development—as epitomized in the phrase, "Ontogeny recapitulates phylogeny"—did impress Darwin, though later research proved that the recapitulation was not as strict as Haeckel believed it to be. He also postulated the existence of a "missing link" between man and his ape-family forebears, to which he gave the name Pithecanthropus. It remained for later scientists to find the bones of the creature to which the name had been applied.

HUMBOLDT, Baron Friedrich Heinrich Alexander von (1769-1859)
German naturalist

Goethe once said of Humboldt: "He possesses . . . a versatility of genius which I have never seen equaled." Packed into Humboldt's incredibly productive 90 years were contributions to neurology, geology, horticulture, philosophy, and oceanography. (The Humboldt Current off the South African coast is so named because of his studies.) More amazing, Humboldt was mainly self-taught in the sciences. In 1799 he began a renowned five-year trip to the Americas, one that in many respects formed the bases for the sciences of physical geography and meteorology. It was an extremely hazardous trip and Humboldt underwent much deprivation. For a while he was even given up for dead. Upon his return to Paris he was revered to an extent usually accorded Napoleon. Some contend that Humboldt's descriptive account of his travels inspired Darwin to enter natural history. Humboldt was the first to establish the use of isotherms (lines joining points on the earth's surface having similar temperatures at

a given time). He also did pioneer work in relating geographic environment and plant distribution and was a leader in building international scientific cooperation. In his seventies he organized his life's knowledge into a five-volume work entitled Kosmos, in which he attempted to assemble the complexities of nature into a rational and unified whole.

HUXLEY, Thomas Henry (1825–1895)
English biologist

Although an eminent scientist in his own right, Huxley is remembered chiefly for having been Darwin's "bulldog," a self-imposed epithet describing his attempts to defend and popularize the views of Darwin, who had an aversion to public feuding. Like so many naturalists, Huxley began in medicine but found the appeal of natural history much greater. In 1851 he was elected to the Royal Society and in 1858 disproved a common theory that the skull

of vertebrates was originally formed out of vertebrae. Shortly thereafter he terminated his own biologic research and devoted full time to publicizing Darwinism. In a famous debate in 1860 with the Bishop of Oxford, Huxley, an agnostic, was asked contumaciously if he traced his simian descent to his father's or mother's side. He responded that given the choice of being related to "a miserable

ape" or a demagogic bishop, "I unhesitatingly affirm my preference for the ape." The bishop left the platform as an ovation for Huxley rose from the audience. In attempting to erect a social philosophy around Darwinism, Huxley met with less success. But he achieved his one great goal—popularizing Darwin.

LAMARCK, Chevalier de (1744–1829)
French naturalist

Although considered the founder of invertebrate zoology, Lamarck is better known for his theory of evolution, an important precursor to Darwin's theory. After disinterested careers in the church and military, Lamarck turned to the study of botany with the encouragement of his friend, Jean Jacques Rousseau, the French philosopher. His work on French flora, published in 1778, was well received and won him admittance to the Academy of Sciences. In 1793, when he was almost 50, he abruptly changed careers by accepting an appointment as professor of zoology at the Museum of Natural History in Paris. He undertook the systematic classification of invertebrates (a term he coined), that portion of the animal kingdom which Linnaeus had naively divided into just two categories: insects and worms. He was the first reputable biologist to devise a truly rational outline for the evolutionary development of life. He postulated that environmental need developed in organisms and were then passed on to offspring—the idea of "acquired characteristics." But Lamarck erred in supposing that animals actually "willed" physical changes, and his theory was generally discredited. Blind and penniless, Lamarck died unappreciated; many years later his contribution was recognized, and Darwin himself admitted, "The conclusions I am led to are not widely different from his."

LINNAEUS, Carolus (1707–1778)
Swedish botanist

It is apt that Linnaeus' name derives from a tall linden tree that grew in the family's garden, for even as a child he possessed a deep interest in trees and flowers. With meager funds he began university studies in medicine and natural science, and while still a student at the University of Uppsala, he conceived a novel way of classifying plants—by their sexual characteristics. He undertook the classification of animals as well, and in time he developed a system of binomial nomenclature, applying genus and species labels to all plants and animals. His system, which was the basis of modern classification in botany and

zoology, gave biologists and evolutionists a framework within which they could analyze living forms and make valid generalizations about them. Daringly for a man of his time, Linnaeus included the orangutan in the same genus as man; nonetheless, he ardently opposed the idea of evolution, believing that no species had changed or become extinct since created by God at the beginning of the world. He wrote his first book at 23 and published more than 180 works in his lifetime. Though he had no doctoral degree, Linnaeus was made professor of anatomy and physics at the University of Uppsala; his reputation drew students to Uppsala from all parts of Europe.

LYELL, Charles (1797–1875)
Scottish geologist

Lyell's entire life, despite his legal training, revolved around geologic interests. An inveterate traveler, Lyell spent years trekking across Europe collecting data to confirm the 18th-century view of James Hutton that the earth was formed by the slow processes of heat and erosion. More of an apologist than a theorizer, Lyell popularized Hutton in an 1830, three-volume work called Principles of Geology. By converting the young Darwin to the belief that the earth was formed by natural causes, Principles in large measure paved the way for Darwin's theories on evolution. In fact, Darwin once confessed feeling that his books "came half out of Sir Charles Lyell's brain." What Lyell had given the great evolutionist was a new geologic time scale, without which, Darwinian scholar Loren C. Eiseley contends, "there would have been no Origin of Species."

By the time that book appeared in 1859, most natural scientists had accepted the implications of Lyell's findings. (Henry Adams once remarked that Lyell had destroyed the Garden

of Eden.) But strangely enough, Lyell had sided with the antievolutionists in the controversy beginning with Lamarck, and it was not until the 1850's that he saw the validity of evolution. By 1863, however, Lyell was ready to take evolutionary views into the realm of man's descent with publication of The Antiquity of Man, thus anticipating Darwin's The Descent of Man by eight years.

MENDEL, Gregor Johann (1822–1884)
Austrian botanist

Born to peasant farmers in Moravia, Mendel pursued his education amid the anxieties of constant poverty. When in 1842, as he wrote, "it was no longer possible to bear up under such deprivations," he entered an Augustinian monastery in Brünn. Sent to the University of Vienna to be trained in science and mathematics, he returned three years later to teach in Brünn. In 1857, in the monastery garden, he began the experiments with pea plants that were to gain him posthumous fame. For eight years, under methodically controlled conditions, he carefully induced pollination in succeeding generations of plants with differing characteristics. He discovered that plants possessed traits that are passed on without change from generation to generation. He demonstrated that when plants were bred to combine specific pairs of traits, the offspring would exhibit these pairs according to a fixed and simple mathematical pattern. Darwin had never been able to explain adequately why variations did not eventually melt into an undistinguished average; Mendel's discoveries of trait-carrying factors (genes) held the answer. But scientists remained ignorant of Mendel's work until 1900, almost two decades after his death (and Darwin's also), when De Vries —and almost simultaneously, two other scientists working independently—found Mendel's monograph on his experiments buried in the scientific archives.

RAY, John (1627–1705)
English naturalist

As a classifier of plants, Ray was precursor to Linnaeus by more than half a century. As a philosopher, however, he was precursor to the religious attacks that would be leveled at Darwin's theory of evolution two centuries later. Trained for the ministry, he lost his right to preach when he refused to sign an affidavit against the Puritans. Turning to natural science, he began to compile a catalogue of plant species that eventually included more than 18,000 entries. He made a significant contribution to the understanding of species, for he recognized that common ancestors, not small differences, were the essential criterion for grouping plants and animals. And yet, despite his familiarity with fossils having no living counterpart, Ray held to a view of immutability of species.

"The number of true species in nature," he declared, "is fixed and limited and, as we may reasonably believe, constant and unchangeable from the first creation to the present day." For a long time thereafter, Ray was a widely read barrier to the acceptance of evolutionary views.

WALLACE, Alfred Russel (1823–1913)
English naturalist

Like Darwin, his contemporary, Wallace began his career as a naturalist with a scientific expedition. In 1848 he journeyed to the Amazon basin, subsequently publishing a report on his travels. Six years later on a trip to the Malay Peninsula and the East Indian islands, Wallace noted a striking difference between the animal species of Asia and Australia. He concluded that the Australian species, being the more primitive, had survived because they had become separated from mainland Asia before the animals there had developed. This led him to ponder the idea of evolution by natural selection at the same time as Darwin. Wallace's ideas, like Darwin's, were reinforced on reading Thomas Malthus, but due to illness Wallace had little time to collect substantiating evidence. Instead, he put his ideas on paper and sent them for criticism and review to a well-known biologist—Charles Darwin. Thunderstruck with the similarity between his and Wallace's conclusions, Darwin offered to share publication with him. Their joint reports first appeared in the Journal of the Linnaean Society in 1858. Wallace's chief contribution to evolution was in biogeography, a science that he systematized in his 1876 work, The Geographical Distribution of Animals. His studies in this field have been commemorated in the name

Wallace's Line, the boundary dividing Asiatic and Australian fauna in the Malay Archipelago.

Weismann, August Friedrich (1834–1914)
German biologist

Weismann was a professor of zoology at the University of Freiburg when, in his middle years, failing eyesight prevented him from using a microscope and forced him into the more theoretical aspects of science. His speculations on evolutionary theory led to an important set of experiments. In an attempt to disprove Lamarck's contention that acquired characteristics can be inherited, Weismann cut off

the tails of more than 1,500 mice over a 22-generation span and then showed that all gave birth to young with completely normal tails. He argued that germ plasm, a basic life-giving substance, was solely responsible for inheritance. The flaw in Weismann's theory was an absence of any room for change, since the germ plasm was postulated to be of one, never-changing variety. Only recently has American biologist Hermann Muller shown that germ plasm is not as isolated as Weismann thought, and that it can actually be modified by the environment, although unpredictably and not by such crude means as mutilating tails.

VOYAGE OF THE BEAGLE

Overwhelmed by the grandeur of a tropical rain forest, which he encountered for the first time in Brazil, Darwin felt a joy so intense that he described it as "a delirium of delight."

On the 27th day of December, 1831, His Majesty's Ship Beagle, a ten-gun brig, set sail from Devonport bound on a five-year scientific voyage around the world. "Never did a vessel leave England better provided or fitted for the service she was destined to perform," boasted her young captain. But what he did not know at the time was that the destiny he spoke of rested chiefly in the fertile mind of an even younger member of the crew, an amateur naturalist named Charles Darwin, who had signed on much against what Captain Fitzroy considered his better judgment. (The captain was an enthusiastic believer in the then popular "science" of physiognomy, and he did not like the look of Darwin's nose, believing it showed a certain sign of laziness.)

During the previous summer, the handsome, 22-year-old Darwin had been doing little more than anticipating the opening of the partridge season when two of his former professors wrote to say that they had recommended him as naturalist for a forthcoming scientific expedition. Darwin was anxious to accept but first had to overcome the strong objections of his father, an irascible country doctor who felt such a trip could contribute nothing to his son's planned career as a clergyman. But young Darwin found an ally in his scientist-uncle, Josiah Wedgwood, who finally persuaded the father to let the son go—a service for which science owes Wedgwood an inestimable debt.

Writing about the trip years later, Darwin described it as "the most important event of my life." In terms of the history of science, it was among the most important events ever. For it was largely from observations made during those five years that Darwin developed his revolutionary theories about the origins of all species, including man.

The following excerpts from Darwin's classic narrative of the trip, The Voyage of the Beagle, recount a number of his more memorable experiences and provide a revealing glimpse into a most remarkable mind during a crucial time of awakening.

BAHIA, BRAZIL, 1832

One of the Beagle's first stops was at Bahia on the Brazilian coast, a region that for Darwin offered both aesthetic and intellectual rewards.

The day has passed delightfully. Delight itself, however, is a weak term to express the feelings of a naturalist who, for the first time, has wandered by himself in a Brazilian forest. The elegance of the grasses, the novelty of the parasitical plants, the beauty of the flowers, the glossy green of the foliage, but above all the general luxuriance of the

vegetation, filled me with admiration. A most paradoxical mixture of sound and silence pervades the shady parts of the wood. The noise from the insects is so loud, that it may be heard even in a vessel anchored several hundred yards from the shore; yet within the recesses of the forest a universal silence appears to reign. To a person fond of natural history, such a day as this brings with it a deeper pleasure than he can ever hope to experience again. . . .

One day I was amused by watching the habits of the Diodon antennatus, which was caught swimming near the shore. This fish, with its flabby skin, is well known to possess the singular power of distending itself into a nearly spherical form. . . .

This Diodon possessed several means of defense. It could give a severe bite, and could eject water from its mouth to some distance, at the same time making a curious noise by the movement of its jaws. By the inflation of its body, the papillae, with which the skin is covered, become erect and pointed. But the most curious circumstance is, that it secretes from the skin of its belly, when handled, a most beautiful carmine-red fibrous matter, which stains ivory and paper in so permanent a manner, that the tint is retained with all its brightness to the present day: I am quite ignorant of the nature and use of this secretion. I have heard from Dr. Allan of Forres, that he has frequently found a Diodon, floating alive and distended, in the stomach of the shark; and that on several occasions he has known it eat its way, not only through the coats of the stomach, but through the sides of the monster, which has thus been killed. Who would ever have imagined that a little soft fish could have destroyed the great and savage shark?

RIO DE JANEIRO, BRAZIL, 1832

For nine months the Beagle *cruised along the eastern coast of South America, with Darwin making frequent inland excursions to examine the exotic flora and fauna. On one such occasion he noted the struggle for survival in the insect world.*

A person, on first entering a tropical forest, is astonished at the labors of the ants; well-beaten paths branch off in every direction, on which an army of never-failing foragers may be seen, some going forth, and others returning, burdened with pieces of green leaf, often larger than their own bodies.

A small dark-colored ant sometimes migrates in countless numbers. One day, at Bahia, my attention was drawn by observing many spi-

Darwin served without pay on the Beagle *(above) in the dual role of ship's naturalist and companion to Robert Fitzroy (below), her autocratic captain.*

141

The acutely observant Darwin noted the unusual defense mechanisms of the Diodontidae family, called, for obvious reasons, porcupine fish. This Diodon, its skin puffed into a balloon studded with tiny barbs, offers would-be aggressors an extremely unpleasant mouthful.

ders, cockroaches, and other insects, and some lizards, rushing in the greatest agitation across a bare piece of ground. A little way behind, every stalk and leaf was blackened by a small ant. The swarm having crossed the bare space, divided itself, and descended an old wall. By this means many insects were fairly enclosed; and the efforts which the poor little creatures made to extricate themselves from such a death were wonderful. When the ants came to the road they changed their course, and in narrow files reascended the wall. Having placed a small stone so as to intercept one of the lines, the whole body attacked it, and then immediately retired. Shortly afterwards another body came to the charge, and again having failed to make any impression, this line of march was entirely given up. By going an inch around, the file might have avoided the stone, and this doubtless would have happened, if it had been originally there: but having been attacked, the lion-hearted little warriors scorned the idea of yielding. . . .

I was much interested one day by watching a deadly contest between a Pepsis and a large spider of the genus Lycosa. The wasp made a sudden dash at its prey, and then flew away: the spider was evidently wounded, for, trying to escape, it rolled down a little slope, but had still strength sufficient to crawl into a thick tuft of grass. The wasp soon returned, and seemed surprised at not immediately finding its victim. It then commenced as regular a hunt as ever hound did after fox; making short semicircular casts, and all the time rapidly vibrating its wings and antennae. The spider, though well concealed, was soon discovered; and the wasp, evidently still afraid of its adversary's jaws, after much maneuvering, inflicted two stings on the under side of its thorax. At last, carefully examining with its antennae the now motionless spider, it proceeded to drag away the body. But I stopped both tyrant and prey.

BAHIA BLANCA, 1832

In Río Negro, Darwin experienced one of the trip's several anxious moments. In retrospect the incident seemed infinitely more humorous.

Our horses were very poor ones, and in the morning they were soon exhausted from not having had any thing to drink, so that we were obliged to walk. About noon the dogs killed a kid, which we roasted. I ate some of it, but it made me intolerably thirsty. This was the more distressing as the road, from some recent rain, was full of little puddles of clear water, yet not a drop was drinkable. I had scarcely been twen-

*Each ant species builds
specialized structures for
its colonies, varying from
chambered mounds to galleried
nests in trees (rear). All
colonies have three social
castes: winged females, who lay
the eggs; winged males, who
die once they have fertilized
the females; and sterile
wingless workers, who toil
at building the nest, finding
food, and tending the precious
grubs that will become
the next generation of ants.*

*Beetle-collecting had been
Darwin's first scientific hobby.
In South America, he matured
as an entomologist, bringing
in as many as 68 beetle species
from a single day's hunt.*

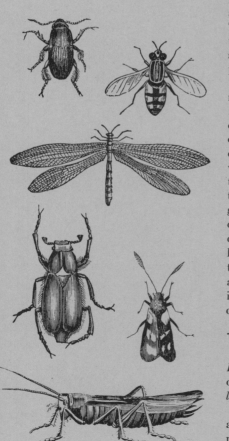

ty hours without water, and only part of the time under a hot sun, yet
the thirst rendered me very weak. How people survive two or three
days under such circumstances, I cannot imagine: at the same time, I
must confess that my guide did not suffer at all, and was astonished
that one day's deprivation should be so troublesome to me. . . .

Two days afterwards I again rode to the harbor; when not far from
our destination, my companion . . . spied three people hunting on
horseback. He immediately dismounted, and watching them intently,
said, "They don't ride like Christians, and nobody can leave the fort."
The three hunters joined company, and likewise dismounted from
their horses. At last one mounted again and rode over the hill out of
sight. My companion said, "We must now get on our horses: load your
pistol"; and he looked to his own sword. I asked, "Are they Indians?"
"*Quién sabe?*" (Who knows?) "If there are no more than three, it does
not signify." It then struck me, that the one man had gone over the
hill to fetch the rest of his tribe. I suggested this; but all the answer I
could extort was, "*Quién sabe?*" His head and eye never for a minute
ceased scanning slowly the distant horizon. I thought his uncommon
coolness too good a joke, and asked him why he did not return home. I
was startled when he answered, "We are returning, but in a line so as
to pass near a swamp, into which we can gallop the horses as far as
they can go, and then trust to our own legs; so that there is no dan-
ger." I did not feel quite so confident of this, and wanted to increase
our pace. He said, "No, not until they do." When any little inequality
concealed us, we galloped; but when in sight, continued walking. At
last we reached a valley, and turning to the left, galloped quickly to
the foot of a hill; he gave me his horse to hold, made the dogs lie down,
and then crawled on his hands and knees to reconnoiter. He remained
in this position for some time, and at last, bursting out in laughter, ex-
claimed, "*Mujeres!*" (Women!).

TIERRA DEL FUEGO, 1833

*Near the southern tip of South America Darwin encountered several
Fuegian natives who no doubt prompted his later remark in* The Descent
of Man: *"For my own part I would as soon be descended from that heroic
little monkey . . . as from a savage who delights to torture his enemies."*

While going one day on shore near Wollaston Island, we pulled
alongside a canoe with six Fuegians. These were the most abject and
miserable creatures I anywhere beheld. On the east coast the natives,

as we have seen, have guanaco cloaks, and on the west, they possess seal-skins. Among these central tribes the men generally have an otter-skin, or some small scrap about as large as a pocket handkerchief, which is barely sufficient to cover their backs as low down as their loins. It is laced across the breast by strings, and according as the wind blows, it is shifted from side to side. But these Fuegians in the canoe were quite naked, and even one full-grown woman was absolutely so. It was raining heavily, and the fresh water, together with the spray, trickled down her body. In another harbor not far distant, a woman, who was suckling a recently born child, came one day alongside the vessel, and remained there out of mere curiosity, while the sleet fell and thawed on her naked bosom, and on the skin of her naked baby! These poor wretches were stunted in their growth, their hideous faces bedaubed with white paint, their skins filthy and greasy, their hair entangled, their voices discordant, and their gestures violent. Viewing such men, one can hardly make oneself believe that they are fellow-creatures and inhabitants of the same world. It is a common subject of conjecture what pleasure in life some of the lower animals can enjoy: how much more reasonably the same question may be asked with respect to these barbarians! . . .

The different tribes have no government or chief; yet each is surrounded by other hostile tribes, speaking different dialects, and separated from each other only by a deserted border or neutral territory: the cause of their warfare appears to be the means of subsistence. Their country is a broken mass of wild rocks, lofty hills, and useless forests: and these are viewed through mists and endless storms. The habitable land is reduced to the stones on the beach; in search of food they are compelled unceasingly to wander from spot to spot, and so steep is the coast, that they can only move about in their wretched canoes. . . . Their skill in some respects may be compared to the instinct of animals; for it is not improved by experience: the canoe, their most ingenious work, poor as it is, has remained the same for the last two hundred and fifty years.

While beholding these savages, one asks, whence have they come? What could have tempted, or what change compelled a tribe of men, to leave the fine regions of the north, to travel down the Cordillera or backbone of America, to invent and build canoes, which are not used by the tribes of Chile, Peru, and Brazil, and then to enter on one of the most inhospitable countries within the limits of the globe? Although

Fuegian Indians endured the savage climate of Tierra del Fuego clad only in skins, or totally naked. They lived in crude shelters (opposite) made from roughly thatched branches. Darwin, appalled by their animal-like existence, found it hard to think of them as fellow human beings.

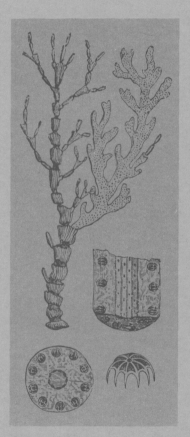

One result of Darwin's voyage was a revolutionary theory about coral reefs, which are built up slowly by the accretion of tiny animals called polyps. Above, the polyps appear as dark circles.

such reflections must at first seize on the mind, yet we may feel sure that they are partly erroneous. There is no reason to believe that the Fuegians decrease in number; therefore we must suppose that they enjoy a sufficient share of happiness, of whatever kind it may be, to render life worth having. Nature by making habit omnipotent, and its effects hereditary, has fitted the Fuegian to the climate and the productions of his miserable country.

VALDIVIA AND CONCEPCION, 1835

Darwin had been studying the elevation and subsidence of South America's coastal regions for several years. While in Valdivia he was thus indeed fortunate—as well as slightly terrified—to experience firsthand the violent earthquake that leveled nearby Concepción in 1835.

This day has been memorable in the annals of Valdivia, for the most severe earthquake experienced by the oldest inhabitant. I happened to be on shore, and was lying down in the wood to rest myself. It came on suddenly, and lasted two minutes, but the time appeared much longer. The rocking of the ground was very sensible. . . . There was no difficulty in standing upright, but the motion made me almost giddy: it was something like the movement of a vessel in a little cross-ripple, or still more like that felt by a person skating over thin ice, which bends under the weight of his body.

I have not attempted to give any detailed description of the appearance of Concepción, for I feel that it is quite impossible to convey the mingled feelings which I experienced. Several of the officers visited it before me, but their strongest language failed to give a just idea of the scene of desolation. It is a bitter and humiliating thing to see works, which have cost man so much time and labor, overthrown in one minute. . . .

The most remarkable effect of this earthquake was the permanent elevation of the land; it would probably be far more correct to speak of it as the cause. There can be no doubt that the land around the Bay of Concepción was upraised two or three feet; but it deserves notice, that owing to the wave having obliterated the old lines of tidal action on the sloping sandy shores, I could discover no evidence of this fact, except in the united testimony of the inhabitants, that one little rocky shoal, now exposed, was formerly covered with water. At the island of S. Maria (about thirty miles distant) the elevation was greater; on one part, Captain Fitzroy found beds of putrid mussel shells *still adhering*

The thirteen almost identical species of finch that Darwin found in the Galápagos Islands were to prove the key to his evolutionary theory. He observed four main groups, differing only in the size of their beaks. Finding only tiny insects to feed upon, the finches at top developed long, sharp beaks. The finch below has a larger beak for larger insects. Beneath is a finch that feeds on small seeds, while the blunt-beaked specimen at bottom can devour big seeds easily.

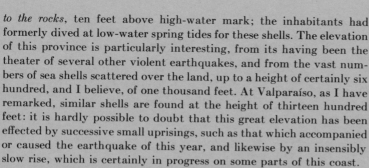

to the rocks, ten feet above high-water mark; the inhabitants had formerly dived at low-water spring tides for these shells. The elevation of this province is particularly interesting, from its having been the theater of several other violent earthquakes, and from the vast numbers of sea shells scattered over the land, up to a height of certainly six hundred, and I believe, of one thousand feet. At Valparaíso, as I have remarked, similar shells are found at the height of thirteen hundred feet: it is hardly possible to doubt that this great elevation has been effected by successive small uprisings, such as that which accompanied or caused the earthquake of this year, and likewise by an insensibly slow rise, which is certainly in progress on some parts of this coast.

GALAPAGOS ARCHIPELAGO, 1835

Among the most important of Darwin's observations were those made on the Galápagos Islands, where he discovered much that perplexed and discomforted him. The wide variety and similarity of plant and animal species seemed to refute the doctrine of special creation and, as Darwin added in his notebook, to "undermine the stability of species."

The natural history of these islands is eminently curious, and well deserves attention. Most of the organic productions are aboriginal creations, found nowhere else; there is even a difference between the inhabitants of the different islands; yet all show a marked relationship with those of America, though separated from that continent by an open space of ocean, between five hundred and six hundred miles in width. The archipelago is a little world within itself, or rather a satellite attached to America, whence it has derived a few stray colonists, and has received the general character of its indigenous productions. Considering the small size of these islands, we feel the more astonished at the number of their aboriginal beings, and at their confined range. Seeing every height crowned with its crater, and the boundaries of most of the lava streams still distinct, we are led to believe that within a period, geologically recent, the unbroken ocean was here spread out. Hence, both in space and time, we seem to be brought somewhat near to that great fact—that mystery of mysteries—the first appearance of new beings on this earth. . . .

Of land birds I obtained twenty-six kinds, all peculiar to the group and found nowhere else, with the exception of one larklike finch from North America (Dolichonyx oryzivorus), which ranges on that continent as far north as 54°, and generally frequents marshes. . . .

In the Galápagos Archipelago Darwin found that reptiles were the highest form of natural life. In addition to the giant tortoises, or galápagos, after which the islands were named, there were several species of lizard, both seagoing and terrestrial, which differed even between one island and the next. Lacking any natural enemies, until the coming of man, these reptiles swarmed about in such quantities that the Beagle's *crew often had to kick them out of the way.*

The most curious fact is the perfect gradation in the size of the beaks in the different species of Geospiza, from one as large as that of a hawfinch to that of chaffinch, and even to that of a warbler. The beak of Cactornis is somewhat like that of a starling; and that of the fourth subgroup, Camarhynchus, is slightly parrot-shaped. Seeing this gradation and diversity of structure in one small, intimately related group of birds, one might really fancy that from an original paucity of birds in this archipelago, one species had been taken and modified for different ends. In a like manner it might be fancied that a bird originally a buzzard, had been induced here to undertake the office of the carrion-feeding Polybori of the American continent. . . .

We will now turn to the order of reptiles, which gives the most striking character to the zoology of these islands. The species are not numerous, but the numbers of individuals of each species are great. . . .

The Amblyrhynchus, a remarkable genus of lizards, is confined to this archipelago. . . . It is extremely common on all the islands throughout the group, and lives exclusively on the rocky sea beaches, being never found, at least I never saw one, even ten yards inshore. It is a hideous-looking creature, of a dirty black color, stupid, and sluggish in its movements. The usual length of a full-grown one is about a yard, but there are some even four feet long; a large one weighed twenty pounds: on the island of Albemarle they seem to grow to a greater size than elsewhere. Their tails are flattened sideways, and all four feet are partially webbed. . . .

I opened the stomachs of several, and found them largely distended with minced seaweed (Ulvae), which grows in thin foliaceous expansions of a bright green or a dull red color. I do not recollect having observed this seaweed in any quantity on the tidal rocks; and I have reason to believe it grows at the bottom of the sea, at some little distance from the coast. If such be the case, the object of these animals occasionally going out to sea is explained. . . . Yet there is in this respect one strange anomaly, namely, that when frightened it will not enter the water. Hence it is easy to drive these lizards down to any little point overhanging the sea, where they will sooner allow a person to catch hold of their tails than jump into the water. They do not seem to have any notion of biting; but when much frightened they squirt a drop of fluid from each nostril. I threw one several times as far as I could, into a deep pool left by the retiring tide; but it invariably returned in a direct line to the spot where I stood. . . . Perhaps this singular piece of apparent stupidity may be accounted for by the circumstance, that this reptile has no enemy whatever on shore, whereas at sea it must often fall a prey to the numerous sharks. Hence, probably, urged by a fixed and hereditary instinct that the shore is its place of safety, whatever the emergency may be, it there takes refuge. . . .

The distribution of the tenants of this archipelago would not be nearly so wonderful, if, for instance, one island had a mocking thrush, and a second island some other quite distinct genus—if one island had its genus of lizard, and a second island another distinct genus, or none whatever—or if the different islands were inhabited, not by representative species of the same genera of plants, but by totally different genera, as does to a certain extent hold good; for, to give one instance, a large berry-bearing tree at James Island has no representative species in Charles Island. But it is the circumstance, that several of the islands possess their own species of the tortoise, mocking thrush, finches, and numerous plants, these species having the same general habits, occupying analogous situations, and obviously filling the same place in the natural economy of this archipelago, that strikes me with wonder. It may be suspected that some of these representative species, at least in the case of the tortoise and of some of the birds, may hereafter prove to be only well-marked races; but this would be of equally great interest to the philosophical naturalist. . . .

The only light which I can throw on this remarkable difference in the inhabitants of the different islands, is, that very strong currents of the sea running in a westerly and west-northwest direction must separate, as far as transportal by the sea is concerned, the southern islands from the northern ones; and between these northern islands, a strong northwest current was observed, which must effectually separate James and Albemarle islands. As the archipelago is free to a most remarkable degree from gales of wind, neither the birds, insects, nor lighter seeds, would be blown from island to island. And lastly, the profound depth of the ocean between the islands, and their apparently recent (in a geological sense) volcanic origin, render it highly unlikely that they were ever united; and this, probably, is a far more important consideration than any other, with respect to the geographical distribution of their inhabitants. Reviewing the facts here given, one is astonished at the amount of creative force, if such an expression may be used, displayed on these small, barren, . . . islands; and still more so, at its diverse yet analogous action on points so near each other.

So well adapted is the Birgus latro *crab for its specialized task of eating coconuts (a habit which Darwin observed in detail), that it lives among the roots of the coco palm and has learned to climb the steep trunk in search of nuts.*

The brutal treatment of slaves in Brazil sickened Darwin, an unusually kind and tender man. It left him with an enduring hatred of an institution that could so demean the human race.

KEELING ISLAND, 1836

In April, 1836, the Beagle *reached Keeling Island in the Indian Ocean, where Darwin was reintroduced to a species of crab whose adaptability, a salient theme in his later works, amazed him.*

I have before alluded to a crab which lives on the coconuts: it is very common on all parts of the dry land, and grows to a monstrous size: it is closely allied or identical with the Birgus latro. The front pair of legs terminate in very strong and heavy pincers, and the last pair are fitted with others weaker and much narrower. It would at first be thought quite impossible for a crab to open a strong coconut covered with husk; but . . . the crab begins by tearing the husk, fiber by fiber, and always from that end under which the three eyeholes are situated; when this is completed, the crab commences hammering with its heavy claws on one of the eyeholes till an opening is made. Then turning around its body, by the aid of its posterior and narrow pair of pincers, it extracts the white albuminous substance. I think this is as curious a case of instinct as ever I heard of, and likewise of adaptation in structure between two objects apparently so remote from each other in the scheme of nature, as a crab and a coconut tree.

PERNAMBUCO, BRAZIL, 1836

Several times during the expedition Darwin became embroiled in heated discussion with Captain Fitzroy over the question of slavery. Darwin's journal reveals his sympathies on the subject.

On the 19th of August we finally left the shores of Brazil. I thank God, I shall never again visit a slave country. To this day, if I hear a distant scream, it recalls with painful vividness my feelings, when passing a house near Pernambuco, I heard the most pitiable moans, and could not but suspect that some poor slave was being tortured, yet knew that I was as powerless as a child even to remonstrate. I suspected that these moans were from a tortured slave, for I was told that this was the case in another instance. Near Rio de Janeiro I lived opposite to an old lady, who kept screws to crush the fingers of her female slaves. I have stayed in a house where a young household mulatto, daily and hourly, was reviled, beaten, and persecuted enough to break the spirit of the lowest animal. I have seen a little boy, six or seven years old, struck thrice with a horsewhip (before I could interfere) on his naked head, for having handed me a glass of water not quite clean; I saw his father tremble at a mere glance from his master's eye. . . .

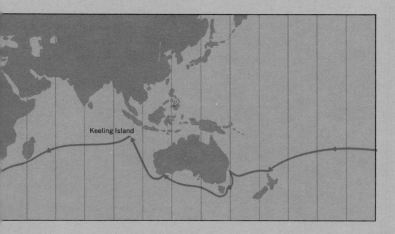

And these deeds are done and palliated by men, who profess to love their neighbors as themselves, who believe in God, and pray that His Will be done on earth! It makes one's blood boil, yet heart tremble, to think that we Englishmen and our American descendants, with their boastful cry of liberty, have been and are so guilty: but it is a consolation to reflect, that we at least have made a greater sacrifice, than ever made by any nation, to expiate our sin.

On the last day of August we anchored for the second time at Porto Praya in the Cape Verde archipelago; thence we proceeded to the Azores, where we stayed six days. On the 2nd of October we made the shores of England; and at Falmouth I left the *Beagle*, having lived on board the good little vessel nearly five years.

ENGLAND, 1836

Looking back on the exhausting trip, Darwin narrates some of its disadvantages.

If a person suffer much from seasickness, let him weigh it heavily in the balance. I speak from experience: it is no trifling evil, cured in a week. If, on the other hand, he take pleasure in naval tactics, he will assuredly have full scope for his taste. But it must be borne in mind, how large a proportion of the time, during a long voyage, is spent on the water, as compared with the days in harbor. And what are the boasted glories of the illimitable ocean? A tedious waste, a desert of water, as the Arabian calls it. . . . It is well once to behold a squall with its rising arch and coming fury, or the heavy gale of wind and mountainous waves. I confess, however, my imagination had painted something more grand, more terrific in the full-grown storm. It is an incomparably finer spectacle when beheld on shore, where the waving trees, the wild flight of the birds, the dark shadows and bright lights, the rushing of the torrents, all proclaim the strife of the unloosed elements. At sea the albatross and little petrel fly as if the storm were their proper sphere, the water rises and sinks as if fulfilling its usual task, the ship alone and its inhabitants seem the objects of wrath. On a forlorn and weather-beaten coast, the scene is indeed different, but the feelings partake more of horror than of wild delight. . . .

But I have too deeply enjoyed the voyage, not to recommend any naturalist, although he must not expect to be so fortunate in his companions as I have been, to take all chances, and to start, on travels by land if possible, if otherwise on a long voyage.

A simplified chart of the Beagle's *route around the world shows the emphasis given to surveying the South American coast line, a task that provided Darwin with invaluable opportunities for his inland exploration. In later years, he described the voyage as "the first real training . . . of my mind."*

BATTLE
OF
THE BONES

FIRST IN THE FIELD: *With hammer in hand and pistols in belt, Professor Othniel C. Marsh, director of Yale's Peabody Museum, stands at the center of a student group bound for the West to hunt for fossils early in the 1870's. After leading six such expeditions in person, Marsh considered the areas he had explored as his exclusive preserve and bitterly resented the encroachment of such fellow fossil hunters as his archrival, Professor Cope of the University of Pennsylvania.*

In the great push west following the Civil War, paleontologists as well as sodbusters were pioneers, and their search for fossils soon resulted in one of the more colorful chapters in the history of scientific discovery.

Foremost in the field were two unusually able men: Othniel Charles Marsh, professor of paleontology at Yale, and Edward Drinker Cope, attached first to the American Philosophical Society and later the University of Pennsylvania. Both were wealthy and both were dedicated collectors: Marsh for Yale's Peabody Museum, built by his uncle; Cope for his personal collections, which filled two Philadelphia town houses to overflowing.

Unfortunately, the two were bitter rivals. Their feud began in 1871, when Cope made an expedition to Kansas, covering ground that Marsh considered exclusively his own. Cope unearthed some astonishing fossils, including a gigantic sea serpent with a neck 20 feet long which he named *Elasmosaurus*. Then Cope moved on to another of Marsh's hunting grounds, in Wyoming, naming a hitherto unknown series of Eocene mammals. To establish priority, Marsh began telegraphing his discoveries back to Yale, and the war was on.

The two accused each other of stealing specimens and of trickery over first publication. If one staked a claim to a particularly rich fossil find, the other moved in at once, luring away field workers by promises of higher pay and, this failing, by threatening violence. The costs rose. Marsh, backed by Peabody money, suffered less than Cope, who beggared himself in the struggle to amass specimens. Smaller collectors were crowded out completely. A Princeton professor, who had contracted to buy a specimen from a nearby farmer, was outmaneuvered by Marsh, who chartered a train from New Haven and snapped up the prize.

In 1890 the quarrel boiled over in the newspapers. Cope accused Marsh of passing off others' work as his own; Marsh ridiculed Cope's tendency to make appalling errors, such as reconstructing *Elasmosaurus* with the head at the wrong end. Within the decade both men died, unreconciled, but their enmity had been amazingly productive: between them they had identified 1,718 new fossil genera and species.

A CREATIVE COLLECTOR: *Edward D. Cope (above) was indefatigable in his pursuit of fossils and brilliant, if sometimes erratic, in re-creating the appearance of long-dead creatures from their bones. Below are his field sketches of two dinosaurs he discovered and named.*

PREHISTORIC WHO'S WHO

ANATOSAURUS
(*an at" o saw' rus*) a giant, duckbilled Cretaceous dinosaur of the swamps. After shoveling up weeds with his huge beak, he ensured easy digestion by chewing them in a mouth containing upwards of 900 teeth.

ALLOSAURUS
(*al" o saw' rus*) a New World dinosaur, this huge, bipedal predator was the tyrant of the Jurassic. He seized his prey in mighty jaws armed with a ferocious set of six-inch-long, saw-edged teeth. His bite was so savage that fossil bones of his contemporaries still bear his teeth marks.

ARCHAEOPTERYX
(*ar" kee op' ter iks*) or "ancient wing," appeared in the Jurassic as the earliest known bird. Comparable in size to a raven and capable of flight, this creature more closely resembled a tiny dinosaur with feathers.

BALUCHITHERIUM
(*ba loo" chi thee' ri um*) a Tertiary rhinoceros who, as the world's largest land mammal, was the size of a double-decker bus. By the merest stretching of the neck, he could easily lunch on twigs and leaves 20 feet above the ground.

BRACHIOSAURUS
(*brack" ee o saw' rus*) about 50 tons, almost 80 feet long, and with a neck stretching 40 feet, he was the biggest dinosaur of them all. Yet despite his fearsome bulk, this was a peaceful monster who spent his days ambling through swamps, dining on vegetation.

COMPSOGNATHUS
(*comp sog' na thus*) no bigger than a chicken, this Jurassic creature was the smallest known dinosaur. Bipedal, he skittered across the ground grasping smaller reptiles in his fore limbs and devouring them with tiny, sharp teeth.

EOHIPPUS
(*ee" o hip' us*) the earliest known horse, whose name is taken from two Greek words meaning "dawn horse." Only a foot high, he scampered through the forests of North America 58 million years ago.

HESPERORNIS
(*hes" per or' nis*) among the earliest of birds, this wingless waterfowl had limbs well-suited to diving and swimming through the Cretaceous seas in search of fish. When he found one, his large jaw, armed with 94 reptilian teeth, made short work of his slithery prey.

ICHTHYORNIS
(*ik" thee or' nis*) a fully-feathered, strong-winged, pigeon-sized bird. His name means "fish-bird," for armed with a large beak containing many sharp teeth, he behaved like a modern sea gull swooping over Cretaceous waters in search of his favorite fare.

ICHTHYOSTEGA
(*ik" thee o staig' a*) a fishlike amphibian who flopped his way onto the land during Devonian time. By developing his fins for movement on land, he became the world's earliest known four-footed animal.

MEGATHERIUM
(*meg" a thee' ri um*) the name means "huge beast" and well it describes this hairy, elephant-sized ground sloth. After wandering from his birthplace in South America, he spent his ice-age days touring Ohio and the Carolinas.

PTERANODON
(*te ran' o don*) a goose-sized flying reptile who, with leathery-skinned wings spanning 20 feet, glided through the Cretaceous skies out over the water, at times straying hundreds of miles from land.

SEYMOURIA
(*see more' ee a*) a three-foot-long, lizard-like creature, the first discovered animal whose physical features were almost exactly intermediate between amphibian and reptile. His remains are found in Permian strata near Seymour, Texas.

XIPHOSURA
(*zif" o sur' a*) a so-called living fossil who has survived with little alteration for 210 million years. When not burrowing under the sand for small organisms, this shelled creature often wanders along the Atlantic shoreline. From his familiar shape this arthropod gets his popular name—the horseshoe crab.

FURTHER READING

Asterisk indicates paperback edition.

PRINCIPLES OF EVOLUTION

Asimov, Isaac. *The Wellsprings of Life.* New York: Abelard-Schuman Limited, 1960.*

Blum, Harold F. *Time's Arrow and Evolution.* Princeton: Princeton University Press, 1955.*

Darwin, Charles. *The Origin of Species and The Descent of Man.* New York: The Modern Library, Inc., 1936.*

Greene, John C. *The Death of Adam.* Ames: The Iowa State University Press, 1959.*

Huxley, Julian. *Evolution in Action.* New York: Harper & Row, Publishers, 1953.*

Olson, E. C. *The Evolution of Life.* London: Weidenfeld, 1965.*

Simpson, George Gaylord. *The Meaning of Evolution.* New Haven: Yale University Press, 1949.*

Simpson, George Gaylord. *Life of the Past.* New Haven: Yale University Press, 1953.

FOSSILS

Andrews, Henry N. *Ancient Plants and the World They Lived In.* Ithaca, N.Y.: Comstock Publishing Co., 1947.

Arnold, Chester A. *An Introduction to Paleobotany.* New York: McGraw-Hill Book Company, Inc., 1947.

Augusta, Joseph, and Zdeněk Burian. *Prehistoric Animals.* London: Spring Books, 1958.

Carrington, Richard. *The Story of Our Earth.* New York: Harper & Row, Publishers, 1956.

Colbert, Edwin H. *Evolution of the Vertebrates.* New York: John Wiley & Sons, Inc., 1955.

Fenton, C. L. and M. A. *The Fossil Book.* Garden City, N.Y.: Doubleday & Company, Inc., 1958.

Hotton, Nicholas III. *Dinosaurs.* New York: Pyramid Publications, Inc., 1963.*

Matthews, William H. *Fossils.* New York: Barnes & Noble, Inc., 1962.*

Romer, Alfred S. *Man and the Vertebrates.* Chicago: University of Chicago Press, 1933.*

Romer, Alfred S. *Vertebrate Paleontology.* (3rd ed.) Chicago: University of Chicago Press, 1966.

Stirton, Ruben Arthur. *Time, Life and Man: The Fossil Record.* New York: John Wiley & Sons, Inc., 1959.

GEOLOGY

Fenton, Carroll Lane. *Earth's Adventures.* New York: The John Day Company, 1942.

Gamow, George. *Biography of the Earth; Its Past, Present, and Future.* New York: The Viking Press, 1959.*

Leet, L. D. and F. J. *The World of Geology.* New York: McGraw-Hill Book Company, Inc., 1961.

Moore, R. C. *Introduction to Historical Geology.* New York: McGraw-Hill Book Company, Inc., 1958.

BIOGRAPHIES

Beer, Gavin de. *Charles Darwin.* Garden City, N.Y.: Doubleday & Company, Inc., 1964.*

George, Wilma. *Biologist Philosopher, A Study of the Life and Writings of Alfred Russel Wallace.* New York: Abelard-Schuman Limited, 1964.

Eiseley, Loren. *Darwin's Century; Evolution and the Men Who Discovered It.* Garden City, N.Y.: Doubleday & Company, Inc., 1958.

Hagberg, Knut. *Carl Linnaeus.* Trans. by Alan Blair. New York: E. P. Dutton & Company, Inc., 1953.

Iltis, Hugo. *Life of Mendel.* New York: W. W. Norton & Company, Inc., 1932.

Lurie, Edward. *Louis Agassiz: A Life in Science.* Chicago: University of Chicago Press, 1960.

Osborn, Henry Fairfield. *Cope, Master Naturalist.* Princeton: Princeton University Press, 1931.

Schuchert, Charles and Clara Mae LeVene. *O. C. Marsh, Pioneer in Paleontology.* New Haven: Yale University Press, 1940.

INDEX

Italics indicate illustrations

A NOTE ON THIS BOOK

This book was published by the Editors of American Heritage Publishing Company in association with the Smithsonian Institution under the following editorial direction: For the Smithsonian Institution, Anders Richter, Director, Smithsonian Institution Press. For American Heritage, Editor, David G. McCullough; Managing Editor, Anthony E. Neville; Art Director, Jack Newman; Assistant Art Director, Donald Longabucco; Copy Editor, Susan M. Shapiro; Assistant Editors, Maria Ealand, Bill Hansen, and Gay Sherry; Picture Editor, Martha F. Grossman; Editorial Assistants, Susan J. Lewis, Nancy Lindemeyer, and Karen Olstad.

PICTURE CREDITS

Cover, Smithsonian Institution; Henry Beville. 2, Walter Dawn. 4, Smithsonian; Henry Beville. CHAPTER I: 6, Galleria Doria; Scala. 8, Muséum National d'Histoire Naturelle. 10, Joyce R. Wilson; Photo Researchers. 13, Caran d'Ache; Bibliothèque Nationale. 15, National Portrait Gallery. 16–17, George John Romanes, *Darwin After Darwin*, 1892. 18, Brown Brothers. 19, N.Y. Public Library. 20–21, Francis & Shaw. CHAPTER II: 22, Lois Crisler. 26–27, Charles J. Ott from National Audubon Society. 29, Cardamone Associates. 31, Copyright © 1952, 1964, William H. Burt and Richard P. Grossenheider, *A Field Guide to the Mammals*, Houghton Mifflin Company, Boston. 33, Cardamone Associates. 34 (top left), Shelly Grossman. 34 (top right), William Jahoda from National Audubon Society. 34 (bottom), Leonard Lee Rue III from National Audubon Society. 35 (top), Charles J. Ott from National Audubon Society. 35 (bottom), Leonard Lee Rue III from National Audubon Society. 36, U.S. Department of the Interior, National Park Service Photo. 38, Frederick C. Baldwin. 40–41, Alfred Sherwood Romer, *Vertebrate Paleontology*, The University of Chicago Press, © 1933, 1945, and 1966 by the University of Chicago, 3rd ed. 42, Courtesy of Parke-Davis. 43, Smithsonian; Henry Beville. CHAPTER III: 44, Department of Vertebrate Paleontology, American Museum of Natural History. 47, Cardamone Associates. 48–49, Richard Erdoes. 50, Smithsonian; Alan Fontaine. 54–55, Jim Stummeier; reprinted from *National Wildlife* magazine, Aug.–Sept., 1967. 57, Culver Pictures. 58–59, Smithsonian; Henry Beville. 61, Smithsonian. CHAPTER IV: 62, copyrighted 1965 William Garnett. 65, Walter Dawn. 66, Francis & Shaw. 68, H. B. Whittington. 69 (left), Robert Dunne; Photo Researchers. 69 (right), Syd Greenberg; Photo Researchers. 70, Andy Bernhaut; Photo Researchers. 71, Shelly Grossman. 73, Alfred Sherwood Romer, *Vertebrate Paleontology*, The University of Chicago Press, copyright 1933 and 1945 by The University of Chicago, 2nd ed. 74–75, Romer, *Vertebrate Paleontology*, 3rd ed. 76, Russ Kinne; Photo Researchers. CHAPTER V: 78, Leonard Lee Rue III from National Audubon Society. 81, Smithsonian; Henry Beville. 82, David Plowden. 83, Larry West. 85, Romer, *Vertebrate Paleontology*, 3rd ed. 87, Jacques Stevens. 88, Romer, *Vertebrate Paleontology*, 2nd ed. 91, Smithsonian; Henry Beville. 93, Annan Photo Features. CHAPTER VI: 94, Bob Goodman; Black Star. 96, Romer, *Vertebrate Paleontology*, 3rd ed. 98, U.S. Department of the Interior, National Park Service Photo. 100–101, Romer, *Vertebrate Paleontology*, 3rd ed. 102–103, Smithsonian; Henry Beville. 105, *The Origin of Birds*, Copyright, 1927, by D. Appleton & Co., renewed, 1955, by Gerhard Heilman. By permission of Appleton-Century, affiliate of Meredith Press. 106, Jack Dermid. 108, Robert F. Sisson, © National Geographic Society. 111, Romer, *Vertebrate Paleontology*, 3rd ed. 113, Smithsonian. PORTFOLIO: 115–116, Smithsonian; Henry Beville. 128, Maria Ealand. APPENDIX: 130 (right), Drawings from *The Fossil Book* by C. L. Fenton and M. A. Fenton, © 1958 by Carroll Lane Fenton and Mildred Adams Fenton, used by permission of Doubleday & Company. 131 (left), Fenton, *The Fossil Book*. 131 (right), Romer, *Vertebrate Paleontology*, 3rd ed. 132 (left), Romer, *Vertebrate Paleontology*, 3rd ed. 132 (right), With permission of John Wiley and Sons, from *Evolution of the Vertebrates*, by Edwin H. Colbert, 1955. 133 (left), Romer, *Vertebrate Paleontology*, 3rd ed. 133 (center), Fenton, *The Fossil Book*. 133 (right), Romer, *Vertebrate Paleontology*, 3rd ed. 134, Francis & Shaw. 135 (both), Culver. 136 (center), Brown Brothers. 136 (right)–139, Culver. 140, *Iconographic Encyclopaedia*, 1851. 141 (top), Burndy Library. 141 (right), Courtesy of the Royal Naval College. 142–144 (left), *The Pictorial Museum of Animated Nature*, Vol. II. 144 (right), Fitzroy, *Narrative of the . . . Beagle*, 1839; N.Y. Public Library. 145, Fitzroy, *Narrative of the . . . Beagle*, 1839; N.Y. Public Library. 146, *The Pictorial Museum of Animated Nature*, Vol. II. 147 (top), Gould, *Zoology of the . . . Beagle*, 1841; N.Y. Public Library. 147 (bottom), Charles Darwin, *Journal of Researches;* N.Y. Public Library. 148, Gould, *Zoology of the . . . Beagle*, 1841; N.Y. Public Library. 149, *The Pictorial Museum of Animated Nature*, Vol. II. 150, Debret, *Voyage . . . au Bresil*, 1834; N.Y. Public Library. 150–151, Cardamone Associates. 151, Burndy Library. 152, Yale-Peabody Museum. 153 (top), Culver. 153 (center and bottom), Courtesy of the American Museum of Natural History.